PHYSIOLOGY OF THE FETUS

Origin and Extent of Function in Prenatal Life

By

WILLIAM FREDERICK WINDLE

Professor of Microscopic Anatomy, Northwestern University Medical School

ILLUSTRATED

W. B. SAUNDERS COMPANY

PHILADELPHIA AND LONDON

1940

Copyright, 1940, by W. B. Saunders Company

MADE IN U. S. A.

PRESS OF
W. B. SAUNDERS COMPANY
PHILADELPHIA

To S. I. KORNHAUSER

PREFACE

MORE than half a century ago Wilhelm Preyer published a monograph "Specielle Physiologie des Embryo" embodying not only a review of the literature of that day, but a great many new observations of his own as well. This book has occupied a rather unique position in that it was long the only source of summarized knowledge concerning the activities of embryos and fetuses of many species. That no other book has quite taken its place is not surprising because, after initial exploration of the field, physiologists turned their attention to more urgent problems concerning the adult. Within the last decade or two, interest has revived and a school of developmental physiology has come into being. Many of the subjects discussed by Preyer have been restudied profitably by experimental methods not available in his time, and new observations have added facts of great significance to our conception of life before birth. Few biologists, however, are aware of all that has been accomplished during the last few years.

My main purpose in writing the present book was to assemble and summarize scattered physiologic observations on fetuses for my own information and for that of my students. I hope that the result will be useful to others who are working in fetal physiology and perhaps will help direct attention to problems which need to be investigated. Another purpose was to provide a supplement for courses in embryology to help stress functional aspects of development; this is in line with current trends of medical teaching. Finally, I had in mind those in allied fields, especially neurology, psychology and pediatrics, who are interested in problems of behavior and who have frequent occasion to desire knowledge of prenatal physiology.

Originally I thought to produce a more comprehensive review somewhat similar to that of Preyer, but my first excursions into fields with which I had been only slightly familiar before demonstrated the futility of doing so within a single small volume. Some of the purposes of the task would have been defeated by undertaking lengthy detailed discussions. Furthermore, a great deal has been written on subjects with which I feel incompetent to deal critically. This is particularly true of nutrition and metabolism. To do justice to these subjects would have meant duplication of much that is contained in Joseph Needham's splendid "Chemical Embryology." Therefore I determined to place emphasis upon the more strictly physiologic aspects of prenatal life and to enter into the chemistry of the fetus only to the point of supplying the reader with brief up-to-date synopses for the sake of completeness.

It is clearly realized that the present book is incomplete in respect to many subjects which might have been included had arbitrary limits not been set down. It was in many instances difficult to draw the line between physiology and anatomy. Determinate growth in the early stages of development was of necessity ignored entirely, and many very interesting observations in experimental embryology of lower vertebrates (indeed, most of the studies in inframammalian species) have been purposely omitted or mentioned only briefly. As much as possible, therefore, I have tried to limit consideration to mammals, and especially to the higher mammals, but I have brought in observations on other animals when these seem to add significantly to our knowledge of human physiology.

Bibliographic references are placed at the end of each chapter. Even though this involves some repetition, it was thought to be a more useful plan than to collect them at the end of the book. Citations have been used freely, but no attempt has been made to include all references on any subject. In most instances, preliminary articles and many of the older papers discussed by Preyer have been left out and only the more recent key references included.

Acknowledgments are due a number of individuals and groups who have contributed directly and indirectly to my program of investigation in fetal physiology and to the present book. In the first place, I am grateful to my teachers and colleagues, especially Professors L. B. Arey, S. W. Ranson and A. C. Ivy, for helpful criticisms and suggestions. My graduate students and associates in research during the past ten years have contributed notably to the project and have provided the incentive to proceed with it. To Sir Joseph Barcroft, in whose laboratory I was a guest during the winter of 1935–36, belongs credit for kindling my interest in respiratory physiology. Finally, to the National Research Council, the Ella Sachs Plotz Foundation, The American Academy of Arts and Sciences, The Child Neurology Research Council (Friedsham Foundation), and The John and Mary R. Markle Foundation, all of whom have generously supplied funds to aid my investigations, I wish to extend thanks.

W. F. WINDLE.

CONTENTS

CHAPTER I

CHAPTER II

CHAPTER III

CHAPTER IV

CHAPTER XV

PHYSIOLOGY OF THE FETUS

CHAPTER I

INTRODUCTION

If one may judge from the number of articles published, there has always been lively scientific interest in the newborn infant. Not only have the functions of its various organs been studied but its behavior has been investigated extensively in order to try to understand normal and abnormal mental processes in the growing individual and the adult. But for the most part, birth has stood as a barrier to our knowledge of the genesis of physiologic functions beyond which little penetration has been made, save by speculation, until recent years. Not alone to the obstetrician, pediatrician and the child psychologist is knowledge of prenatal function and behavior a subject of importance. Physiology of the fetus bears much the same relationship to adult physiology as structural embryology bears to the anatomy of the adult and should be a serious concern of all.

In casting about among the scattered accounts of observations pertaining to physiology during development one finds a wide choice of experimental material. Many forms of animals have been studied. We are particularly concerned with conditions encountered in mammals, especially the true mammals. Most noteworthy investigations have employed fetuses of the ordinary laboratory and domestic animals and man, but less common species have been used occasionally. Observations in the opossum and in lower vertebrates, *i.e.,* birds, reptiles, amphibia and fishes, have contributed very significant information on function during development. It is always necessary to proceed cautiously in attempting to interpret human fetal behavior in terms of results obtained in lower forms. Activities engaged in by immature individuals of any animal forecast the adult physiology of that particular species and are less distinctly related to others. They are often influenced by very special conditions peculiar to the species and not so evident in higher or lower forms. Even among the true mammals there is no uniformity of fetal behavior. In the first place it varies in respect to the manner in which respiration, nutrition and elimination are provided. Significant differences in placentation must be given consideration.

RELATION OF FETAL TO MATERNAL ORGANISM

The fertilized ovum requires several days for transit down the uterine tube to the uterus in most mammals and, during the while, it undergoes development from a single cell to many cells.

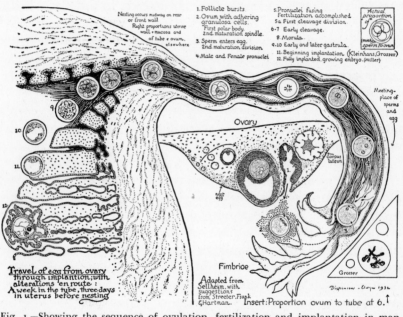

Fig. 1.—Showing the sequence of ovulation, fertilization and implantation in man. (Dickinson, R. L.: "Human Sex Anatomy," Williams and Wilkins, Publishers.)

An efficient placental mechanism is unnecessary to meet the requirements of this early growth. About ten days elapse between fertilization and implantation in man and in this period the ovum forms into a fluid filled blastocyst not a great deal larger than the single unfertilized cell (Fig. 1). All mammals begin to develop a placenta at about this stage to provide nourishment and oxygen for further growth. But the efficiency of exchange between fetus and mother varies greatly and the functional activities which one encounters in studying the fetus are influenced correspondingly.

Intimacy of relationship between fetal and maternal tissues is unequally established in the uteri of different mammals. A graded series can be arranged on the basis of the number of tissues which separate the fetal blood from that of the mother.[1] In marsupials, such as the opossum, only a simple contact is formed; the outer chorionic surface of the blastocyst rests against the unbroken epithelium of the uterus. This is the least efficient relationship, one in which materials must pass through two layers of capillary endothelium, two layers of epithelium, two layers of connective tissue and the potential lumen of the uterus in their course from one organism to the other. Formation of chorionic villi characterizes the union of fetus with the uterus in all the true mammals, but this does not in itself offer great improvement in efficiency unless some of the tissue barriers are broken down. In the horse and pig a diffuse arrangement of villi prevails in a simple epithelio-chorial placenta in which there is no erosion of maternal tissues. The villi simply make contact with the uterine epithelium and are bathed in secretions and transudates which form the "uterine milk" (Fig. 2, *A*).

The ruminating mammals, such as cattle, sheep and deer, have developed a little better arrangement in the placenta. The chorionic villi dip into the uterine glands and an incomplete breakdown of the uterine epithelium occurs between villi (Fig. 2, *B*). Consequently there are regions in the cotyledonary syndesmochorial placenta of these animals wherein exchange is effected through one less layer of tissue than in the pig. But contact between fetus and host is quite simple and there is no tearing of the maternal tissues when the two separate at birth.

The first true deciduate placenta appears in carnivores, such as the dog and cat. Erosion of the uterine mucosa is effected by some means not at all understood although assumed by many to be by ferments liberated in the chorionic epithelium. The fetal blood stream coursing in the chorionic villi is separated from the maternal stream by the tissues of the villi and by the maternal capillary endothelium (Fig. 2, *C*). Tearing of uterine mucosa is encountered at birth when this endothelio-chorial placenta comes away.

In the hemo-chorial placentas of man and the other primates as well as insectivores and lower rodents the process of erosion of

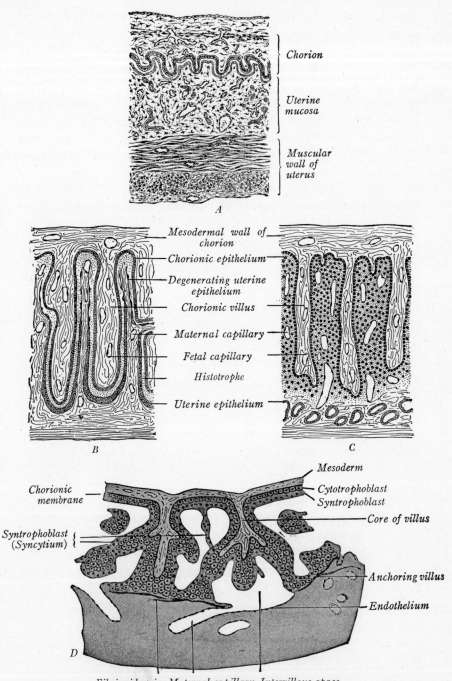

Fig. 2.—Diagrammatic sections through the placentas of (*A*) the pig, (*B*) the cow, (*C*) the cat, and (*D*) man. (Arey: "Developmental Anatomy.")

uterine mucosa by the chorionic villi results in the opening of maternal blood channels.* Consequently fetal blood is separated from that of the mother by only the tissues of the villi themselves (Fig. 2, *D*). An even more efficient hemo-endothelial placenta has been developed by the higher rodents, such as the rat, guinea pig and rabbit,[4] and in it the fetal capillaries are separated from maternal blood by no tissues other than their own endothelium. Placental classifications compiled from studies of Grosser[1] and Mossman[5] are summarized in Table 1.

TABLE 1

TISSUES AND SUBSTANCES SEPARATING FETAL FROM MATERNAL BLOOD IN FIVE TYPES OF PLACENTAS

Type of placenta	Epithelio-chorial	Syndesmo-chorial	Endothelio-chorial	Hemo-chorial	Hemo-endothelial
Maternal tissue:					
Endothelium...	+	+	+	−	−
Connective....	+	+	−	−	−
Epithelium....	+	−	−	−	−
Uterine milk or pablum.......	+	+	−	−	−
Fetal tissue:					
Chorion.......	+	+	+	+	−
Mesenchyme...	+	+	+	−	−
Endothelium...	+	+	+	+	+
Examples.......	Horse, swine	Cattle, sheep	Cat, dog	Man, monkey	Rabbit, guinea pig, rat

It must be remembered also that there is a certain degree of recapitulation of placental history during development. The rabbit whose fully formed placenta is of the hemo-endothelial type has essentially a hemo-chorial or perhaps even a syndesmo-chorial placenta earlier, as will be seen in Table 2. A yolk-sac placenta is often present as a transient supplementary structure, but it may persist and function concurrently throughout gestation as has been demonstrated in the rat.[6, 7]

Time and again in the study of prenatal physiology it will appear that species variations in the intimacy between maternal and

* Bartelmez[2, 3] has reported that the intervillous space of the human and monkey placentas contains little blood. He suggests that an active flow of tissue fluid from the neighboring maternal capillaries fills this space from which it is expelled by rhythmical contractions of the uterus.

fetal blood streams may explain differences in experimental results. Perhaps some of these are real but others seem to be artifac-
tual. Opening the uterus and exposing a fetus with an epithelio-
chorial placenta, whose contact with the host is slight, can be
expected to disturb respiratory exchange and other functions more
readily than the same procedure in one with a hemo-chorial or
hemo-endothelial placenta. The fundamental species differences
in placentation have not often been given adequate consideration
in attempting comparative interpretation of data.

TABLE 2

TISSUES SEPARATING FETAL FROM MATERNAL BLOOD IN THE RABBIT PLACENTA AT
VARIOUS AGES

Age in days	8	10	17	28
Maternal tissue:				
Endothelium...............	+	−	−	−
Connective.................	+	−	−	−
Epithelium.................	−	−	−	−
Fetal tissue:				
Chorion...................	+	+	+	−
Mesenchyme...............	+	+	−	−
Endothelium...............	+	+	+	+

Functional variations in early prenatal life may be related to
other differences in development of the fetal membranes. For
example, the allantois, aside from playing an important part in
providing vascularization of the ectoplacenta, is concerned to a
variable extent in storing and absorbing fetal excretions. In many
mammals including man this organ is of little consequence because of its rudimentary nature. But in others, such as the pig,
sheep and cat, it is highly developed. It has been suggested[8] that
those with large allantoic vesicles have large functional mesonephros and inadequate provision for early placental elimination, a
concept which has recently been questioned.[9]

It is known that the activities of the uterus itself bring about
changes in prenatal function. Disturbance of normal uterine tone
alters the behavior of the fetuses. Thus we find that immobiliza-
tion of the uterus during the late stages of gestation by unbalanc-
ing its hormonal control makes possible the observation of somatic
activities characteristically seen earlier during conditions of anoxemia.[10] There is some evidence that the rhythmical contraction

and relaxation of the uterine musculature which is found toward the end of pregnancy serves to vary the oxygenation of the fetal blood.[11] A few attempts have been made to correlate uterine motility with changes in other physiologic functions of the fetus but much remains to be determined.

The normal physiology of the uterus and placenta must be considered in choosing an animal for investigation in fetal physiology. But these are by no means the only factors. It is important to take account of the rate of embryonic growth, which may be so rapid that a graded fetal series at the various functional stages is difficult to assemble. Some species are more mature at birth than others: contrast the guinea pig with the newborn kitten for example. Lengths of gestation of the principal forms to be considered will be found in Table 3.

TABLE 3

GESTATION PERIODS OF MAMMALS IN WHICH FETAL STUDIES HAVE BEEN MADE

Species	Duration	Species	Duration
Opossum	13 days	Pig	17 weeks
Mouse	20 "	Sheep	21 "
Rat	21 "	Goat	21 "
Rabbit	32 "	Monkey (Macac)	24 "
Dog	63 "	Man	38 "
Cat	65-67 "	Cow	40 "
Guinea pig	67-69 "	Horse	48 "

Fetal structural differences account for many of the functional variations which are encountered in studying different species of animals. For example, one can not expect to observe the development of the characteristically anthropoid hand and foot reflexes in the embryos of hoofed animals. However, it is often more important to use fetuses of large size than small ones whose morphology and placental physiology are more similar to man. But here again it may be impossible to draw deductions concerning such functions as those of the endocrine glands in the human fetus from experiments in the cow or sheep whose placentas are less permeable to molecules of large size than is that of man. Consequently, selection of the experimental material must be made critically to fit the problem under consideration.

EXPERIMENTAL METHODS

Fully as important as selection of suitable specimens for the investigation is the employment of an experimental method which will interfere as little as possible with normal functions of both maternal and fetal organisms. Many of the earlier studies in fetal behavior appear to have been conducted without benefit of anesthesia,[12] a practice whose use today is limited to the most minor surgical procedures. It is usually essential that the pregnant animal be rendered unconscious and this can be accomplished by one of a number of methods.

Some experiments can be conducted under a general anesthetic such as ether, urethane or one of the barbituric acid compounds. However, it is very important to consider the action of these drugs upon the uterus and the fetus and to decide whether or not and to what extent the functions to be investigated will be influenced by them. In many instances this has not been done and results have consequently been wrongly interpreted.

A local anesthetic may be satisfactory to insure quiescence of the maternal animal when given either in the form of cutaneous infiltration with cocaine solutions or as an intradural injection. Some species lend themselves to such treatment better than others but there is always the danger, especially with cutaneous injection, of the animals becoming restless and interfering with observations in the fetuses at a critical moment.

Some investigators have preferred to section the spinal cord at a high level and under a general anesthetic preliminary to making observations in the fetuses. It is essential to allow sufficient time to elapse after the operation not only for recovery from the anesthesia but to overcome the effects of shock. When this has been done the animals, although conscious, can be operated upon without further treatment because sensations are no longer perceived from the region below the spinal transection and the specimens are immobilized by paralysis.

A method which in many respects is more satisfactory for fetal studies is that involving anemic decerebration.[13] It has been used most successfully in cats but has likewise been adapted to rats[14] and can be used in other species with certain modifications. The animals are first anesthetized with ether. The carotid arteries are ligated high in the neck, making certain that the blood

flow to the brain from these sources is stopped. A tracheal cannula is inserted to facilitate the next stage in the operation. After
incising and retracting the soft palate and mucous membrane on
the roof of the pharynx, a small hole is drilled through the
cranium between the two tympanic bullae and the dura mater is
torn to allow the cerebrospinal fluid to escape. A ligature is then
passed around the basilar artery at about the middle of the pons
and this vessel is tied. This method of decerebration renders the
animals unconscious without significant loss of blood and without seriously disturbing other physiologic functions. There is no
evidence of surgical shock, for continuous records of the animals'
blood pressures taken during the operation show no depression.[15]
A variable degree of decerebrate rigidity appears when the ether
is discontinued after the operation. Respiration is usually slowed
but increases in rate during the course of an hour or more which
should be allowed for complete recovery from the anesthetic. As
a rule the rate is normal or faster than normal by the time of experimentation. Consciousness is lost, the animals usually are un-
responsive to manipulation of the viscera and there is no further
need for anesthesia.

Even under the best of experimental conditions it is exceedingly difficult if not actually impossible to expose and maintain
fetuses in a state comparable with that in utero. An attempt is
usually made to deliver them without separating the placenta
from the uterine wall and some investigators have assumed that
by doing so respiration and nutrition of the specimens are pre-
served at normal levels. This is seldom the case because efficiency
of the placental exchange becomes seriously impaired by changing
the spatial and pressure relationships with incision of the uterus
and subsequent removal of part of its contents. Furthermore, it
seems probable that the less intimate the contact between maternal
and fetal parts of the placenta, the greater are the chances that
opening the uterus will upset physiologic conditions in the fetuses.
These facts must be faced and results interpreted accordingly.

It is essential to realize first of all that the behavior exhibited
by fetuses at experimental hysterotomy, even when the placentas
are allowed to remain attached, is not that occurring within the
undisturbed uterus but is affected by the partial anoxemia attendant upon the experimental procedure.[15] However, in many

instances the purpose of the experiment is to determine what functions the fetus is capable of performing and not what it may actually do. Consequently it is not essential to preserve the placental mechanism in perfect physiologic condition for long.

The problems involved in most investigations in physiology of the fetus are complicated because one is dealing with two organisms maintaining mutual although precarious relationships to one another. It is true that the fetus cannot be studied under physiologic conditions when the health of the mother is jeopardized, but on the other hand the best of conditions in the mother do not insure that behavior of the extracted fetuses will always be normal. Only by understanding the fundamentals of physiology of respiration, circulation, metabolism, etc., in the adult can one hope to arrive at significant information concerning similar functions in prenatal life. Gradually problems occasioned by the inaccessibility of the fetus which have baffled investigators in the past are being solved through the invention of new and ingenious technical procedures.

REFERENCES CITED

1. Grosser, O. 1927. Frühentwicklung, Eihautbildung und Placentation. Bergmann, München.
2. Bartelmez, G. W. 1931. Anat. Rec., 48: Suppl. 9.
3. Bartelmez, G. W. 1935. Ibid., 61: Suppl. 4.
4. Mossman, H. W. 1937. Contr. Emb., 26: 129.
5. Mossman, H. W. 1926. Am. J. Anat., 37: 433.
6. Brunschwig, A. E. 1927. Anat. Rec., 34: 237.
7. Everett, J. W. 1935. J. Exp. Zoöl., 70: 243.
8. Bremer, J. L. 1916. Am. J. Anat., 19: 179.
9. Gersh, I. 1937. Contr. Emb., 26: 33.
10. Windle, W. F., M. Monnier & A. G. Steele. 1938. Physiol. Zoöl., 11: 425.
11. Windle, W. F. & A. G. Steele. 1938. Proc. Soc. Exp. Biol & Med., 39: 246.
12. Preyer, W. 1885. Specielle Physiologie des Embryo, Grieben, Leipzig.
13. Pollock, L. J. & L. E. Davis. 1924. Arch. Neur. Psychiat., 12: 288.
14. Windle, W. F. & W. L. Minear. 1933. Anat. Rec., 57: 1.
15. Windle, W. F. & R. F. Becker. 1940. Arch. Neur. Psychiat., 43: 90.
16. Dickinson, R. L. 1933. Human Sex Anatomy, Williams & Wilkins, Baltimore (ref. for Fig. 1).
17. Arey, L. B. 1940. Developmental Anatomy, Saunders, Philadelphia (ref. for Fig. 2).

CHAPTER II

THE FETAL HEART

INITIATION OF THE HEART BEAT

WHILE the embryo consists of an aggregate of relatively few cells there is no need of a special mechanism to circulate oxygen laden blood. Tissue respiration of the ovum is adequately supported by the gas tension gradients between maternal fluids and embryonal cells at the site of implantation; nutritional needs are slight. But with further growth in size the usefulness of a circulatory system becomes evident.

Until recently the earliest contractions of the mammalian heart had not been seen. Although many investigators[1-3] have studied chick embryos incubated less than two days Sabin[4] and Johnstone[5] appear to have been the first to watch the initiation of the beat at the ten somite stage. It was found that contractions begin on the right side of the ventricle at a point near its junction with the primordium of the atrium. It seemed to these observers that the earliest contractions occurred rhythmically. More recently others[6] have extended this work in a very painstaking cinematographic study. They discovered that the first beats are arrhythmical fibrillations of a few cells located in the bulbo-ventricular region of nine somite embryos. The atrial myocardium shows no activity until three or four hours after contractions have started in the ventricles; the sinus venosus begins to beat still later. Synchronized rhythmical contractions of the entire ventricle result from coalescence of the early fibrillations of right and left sides. The earliest agitation of ventricular contents is simply tidal. Blood is not propelled directionally by the early cardiac activity but its movement begins before the beat has involved the still incompletely fused sinus venosus. When contractions of the atrium start they are faster than those of the ventricle. With coalescence of activity in the atrium and ventricle there results an acceleration of the rate of the ventricular beat. Similarly the contractions of the sinus venosus, when added to those of the ventricle and atrium, bring about a second acceleration.

The genesis of contractions of the mammalian heart has been observed in hanging-drop cultures of whole embryonic vesicles of rats.[7] The beat begins at the three somite stage before the primitive myocardial tubes have fused. Thus the heart starts to function at an earlier time in the rat, relatively, than in the chick embryo. Three or four cells of the left ventricular primordium,

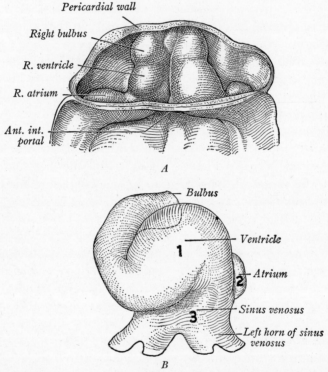

Fig. 3.—The heart of human embryos of (A) 6 somites and (B) 11 somites. The heart begins to beat in mammalian embryos comparable with A. The order of initiation of the beat is shown in B by the figures 1 (ventricle), 2 (atrium) and 3 (sinus venosus). (Arey: "Developmental Anatomy.")

near its junction with the future atrium, begin to contract rhythmically (Fig. 3, A). About two hours later a slower rhythm starts in the right ventricular tube, retaining an independent beat until the two sides fuse (Fig. 3, B). When this occurs the left side dominates the right and becomes the pacemaker in establishing a single wave-like ventricular contraction; some variations were encountered. Atrial contractions begin later than do those of the ventricular tubes. It was impossible to determine the existence of earlier, arrhythmical contractions like those seen in the chick embryo; perhaps failure to observe them can be explained on the basis of technical differences in the two investigations.

The initiation of the heart beat has been studied in amphibian embryos where, in general, the observations on birds and mammals have been confirmed.[8] The first activity occurs in different parts of the ventricle in different specimens. Most of the embryonic amphibian hearts exhibit rhythmicity in the earliest stages of beating.

It was held for many years that the cardiac beat has its origin in the sino-atrial region and that this region remains the pacemaker thereafter.[9, 10] The recent studies in amphibian, bird and mammalian embryos demonstrate that this is not the case. By cutting the embryonic heart between ventricle and sinus venosus it has been found that the beat of the ventricle remains unaltered unless contractions have already begun in the other parts, in which case the two pieces of tissue take up independent rhythms.[5, 6, 8, 11] The intrinsic beat of the sinus venosus is faster than that of the atrium, which in turn is faster than that of the ventricle. Each newly acquired contracting portion when added to older parts sets a faster pace for them. It may be concluded that although the heart beat has its genesis in the ventricular region and not in the sinus venosus, regulation of the ventricular beat is brought under control of the sino-atrial region very early in development.

THE FETAL ELECTROCARDIOGRAM

A number of attempts have been made to record action currents of the human fetal heart near term by means of the electrocardiograph, the investigators using leads placed on the mother's abdomen and in the vagina or rectum.[12–19] Similar studies have been undertaken in the horse.[20] The records obtained have been of little value for interpreting events of conduction in the fetal heart because the deflections were small. The fetal electrocardiogram at 9 months is said to exhibit a simple upright monophasic curve.[21] More recently however electrocardiograms have been obtained from younger human fetuses removed at operation.[22, 23] In the three conventional leads the records showed all deflections of the adult. The most significant difference between human electrocardiograms at birth and in the adult is that the newborn right ventricle exhibits a definite functional preponderance.[24, 25] This is correlated with the fact that the right ventricle outweighs the left by 13 per cent in full term fetuses.[26] Left ventricular preponderance begins to become evident at about the second or third postnatal month, and by the sixth month of life one can scarcely see any difference between electrocardiograms of infants and adults. These observations signify that the left side of the heart becomes larger than the right by the second or third month. It is doubtful if this comes about in those infants in which the ductus arteriosus remains patent for several weeks or months after birth and consequently allows the blood pressure on the two sides to equalize.

The developing bird's heart offers the best opportunity to examine action currents critically under controlled conditions. A number of investigations have been made in the chick but only two merit consideration here. In one series of experiments[27] small holes were drilled through the shell of incubating eggs and electrodes were inserted without disturbing the embryos. The eggs were then placed in a special incubator and allowed to remain quietly for some time before electrical records were made. In the other series[28] the eggs were opened, blastoderms removed and placed in a special chamber. A micromanipulator was used to place the electrodes upon the embryo. Amplification was employed in both cases.

The first deflections of the galvanometer were obtained from chicks of 15 somites (33 to 36 hours incubation) in which the heart consists almost entirely of ventricle. This is not much later than the time of initiation of rhythmical heart beats. The first curves showed none of the deflections which characterize the adult but appeared as simple deflections first below, then above the isolectric line (Fig. 4). In slightly older, 16 somite embryos a sharp downward deflection followed by a rapid return to or above the line appeared; this resembled the Q R S complex. The auricular deflection (P) did not appear until about 42 hours incubation, i.e., soon after the auricular beats had become established, and it was first seen as a downward deflection (Fig. 5). Later the P wave reversed. These results correlate nicely with what has been learned from direct observations of the developing chick heart.[6]

By the fourth day of incubation the embryonic electrocardiogram was practically identical with that of the adult hen. This is a remarkable observation for there are no nerves in the heart at this

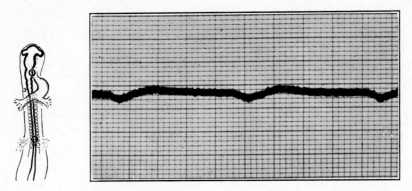

Fig. 4.—Electrocardiogram from a 15 somite chick embryo (±36 hours incubation). The diagram on the left of this and of Fig. 5 shows the shape of the heart and position of the leads. (Hoff, et al.: Am. Heart J., Vol. 17, 1939, C. V. Mosby Co.)

time and the special tissue of the cardiac conduction system is not as yet distinguishable. Time relationships taken from electrocardiograms of the chick will be found in Table 4.[27]

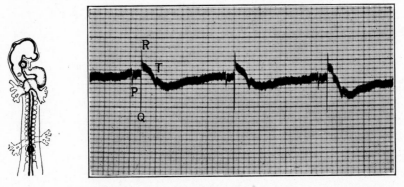

Fig. 5.—Electrocardiogram from a 20 somite chick embryo (± 42 hours incubation). Compare with Fig. 4. (Hoff, et al.: Am. Heart J., Vol. 17, 1939, C. V. Mosby Co.)

THE FETAL PULSE RATE

The pulse rate of chick embryos has been studied on a number of occasions, but most of the results are open to the criticism that temperature and mechanical factors were not controlled pre-

TABLE 4

TIME RELATIONSHIPS CALCULATED FROM ELECTROCARDIOGRAMS OF THE CHICK

Age	Length of heart	Heart rate	P-R interval	Duration of R rise	Duration of R-T complex	Approximate conduction speed
	mm.	per min.	sec.	sec.	sec.	mm./sec.
40 hr. embryo	0.8	120	none	.009–.012	0.28–0.32	2.67
60 hr. embryo	1.2	163	0.11	.008–.010	0.20–0.21	3.80
120 hr. embryo	2.0	230	0.09	.010	0.21–0.24	6.35
5 day chick	14.0	295	0.06	.004–.006	0.24–0.33	40.58
Adult hen	40.0	320	0.06	.009	0.15–0.18	117.77

cisely during experiments. The studies of Cohn and Wile[29] and especially those of Bogue[30] are the most significant. The latter recorded heart beats electrically from undisturbed eggs at a temperature which fluctuated no more than 0.25° C. It was found

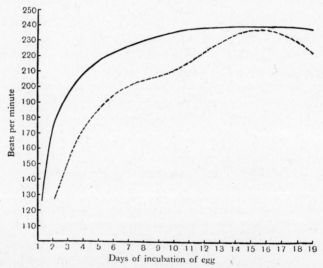

Fig. 6.–Heart rate during incubation of the chick. The solid line: Bogue's data; broken line: Cohn and Wile. (Bogue: J. Exp. Biol., Vol. 9, 1933.)

that the heart rate rises sharply in early stages of incubation, increases more slowly from the tenth day onward to hatching, shows another rapid elevation at hatching and thereafter is maintained nearly at a constant level throughout life. Average heart rates in chick embryos are illustrated graphically in Fig. 6. Bogue found

that very slight temperature differences had a marked direct effect
upon the embryonic pulse rate. He could find no relationship
between the sex and pulse rate of chick embryos nor could a close
correlation between metabolic rate and pulse rate be demonstrated. It may be significant that a physiologic anoxemia is imposed upon the chick toward the end of incubation; this can have
a direct inhibitory action upon the pacemaker mechanism. The
acceleration immediately after hatching may represent a release
from the anoxemia.

Because of its great importance in obstetrics, the human fetal
heart rate has been studied extensively. It is well established that
the average frequently at term is 130 to 150 beats per minute. Extremes of 110 and 180 are commonly observed but a rate of less
than 100 should be viewed with alarm. The average heart rate
encountered in premature infants (about 120 per min.) is slower
than that of infants at full term.[31] The fetal heart slows during
birth but accelerates when respirations begin and may be maintained at 170 to 180 beats per minute for fifteen to thirty minutes
thereafter.[32]

Few systematic correlations of the human heart rate with fetal
age have been made. In fact very little reliable information is
available for any mammal. It is impossible to detect human fetal
heart sounds accurately before about the fifth month. The human
fetal heart beats faster in mid-fetal life than it does just before
birth.[33] A steady decline from a mean of 156 beats per minute
at the fifth lunar month to 142 at the ninth, and a slight subsequent increase during the tenth month have been observed in one
series of thirty subjects.

In rat embryos which had been exposed by opening the uterus
it was found[34] that the heart rate fluctuated widely throughout
pregnancy and was slower than but ran parallel to that of the
mother. Only roughly did the data indicate an increase in frequency from early to late prenatal stages. During late fetal life of
the dog, ox, goat and man the heart beats faster than it does in the
young offspring after birth. A gradual decline is observed from
infancy to maturity. This is illustrated in Table 5, compiled from
observations of several investigators.[29, 33-37]

The adult rate appears to be higher than the fetal rate during
the latter part of gestation in the rat[34] and monkey,[35] resembling

TABLE 5
HEART RATE IN FETAL, NEWBORN AND ADULT ANIMALS

	Early fetus	Late fetus	Newborn	Adult
Hen.............	120–170	220–264	295	320
Rat.............	96–114	123–248	...	184–280
Goat.............	....	120–246	145–240	...
Ox.............	....	161	141	50
Dog.............	....	120–170	160	100
Monkey.........	....	100–180	...	140–240?
Man............	156	130–150	112	70

the bird in this respect. The possibility of asphyxial depression of the fetal heart in the rat experiments should be borne in mind, although most of the fetal heart rates were not abnormally slow in comparison with other species of animals. The adult rat, being an example of a small animal with rapid pulse rate, may not actually develop the inhibitory mechanism to the same degree found in larger mammals. The rapid maternal pulse of the adult monkey was attributed to the animal's excitement and exertion.

NERVOUS CONTROL OF THE FETAL HEART AND CIRCULATION

It is thought that the progressive slowing of the pulse in postnatal life is associated with improvement of control of the heart by the vagus nerves. It has been pointed out that animals with small hearts have rapid pulse rates and those with large hearts have slower rates.[37] Control by the vagus is less pronounced in the former than in the latter. The higher metabolic rate of small animals is thought to make it necessary for the heart to beat about as fast as it can under normal circumstances; consequently there should be no call for an active inhibitory mechanism.

Perhaps the fetal heart rate is rapid because nervous control has not become well established or is inhibited in some way. Most of the evidence points to the conclusion that vagus function is not nearly so marked in the fetus as it is in the adult, although considerable species variation is encountered. Stimulation of the vagus nerves in the chick had no effects at 18 to 20 days of incubation, but it slowed the beat seven to eight hours after hatching.[38] Inhibition was effected by direct stimulation of the heart itself in embryos of five days incubation.[39] Muscarin produced the same result in even younger chick embryos; it slowed the heart of small rat embryos and was antagonized by atropine. These results indicate that the failure to obtain inhibition of the heart by vagus stimulation is not due to factors inherent in the myocardium.

Most investigators who have studied the phenomenon of vagus inhibition in young postnatal mammals have been able to produce slowing or cessation of the heart beat by stimulating the peripheral cut end of the nerve, but in many instances the effects seem to have been weaker than would have been obtained in adults.[40–45] This was especially true in experiments with kittens.[41] The nearer to birth, postnatally, the less the chance of producing inhibition by stimulating the vagus nerves. In one newborn rabbit which showed no cardiac slowing upon stimulation of the peripheral vagus, respiratory inhibition was demonstrated by stimulating the central end, indicating that the nerve is capable of conducting and that conduction can take place through medullary centers at birth.[45] In prenatal life a few successes as well as many failures have been reported in several species.[40, 41, 45, 46] It is probable that the negative results were obtained in many instances because the vagus nerves had been stimulated only after a maximum decline in the rate of the heart beat had occurred in consequence of asphyxia.

In experiments with rabbits Bauer[47] has found that stimulation of the vagus nerve increases the decline in heart rate which is brought about by asphyxia. This was not demonstrable however until about the fourth day after birth. Clamping the umbilical cord at experimental Caesarean section led almost immediately to asphyxial bradycardia, but the phenomenon was delayed in specimens which had breathed air and in which asphyxia was subsequently produced by occluding the trachea. The amount of oxygen available in the blood was greater in the latter than in the former instance. The asphyxial slowing of the fetal heart rate appeared to be due, not to influence of the central nervous system effected through the vagus nerves, but to a direct chemical action upon the pacemaker of the heart.

Various theories have been proposed to explain the slowing of the human fetal heart at the time of delivery. Compression of the skull of young rabbits produces bradycardia and some have held that the passage of the fetal head through the birth canal may bring about enough pressure to cause a similar cardiac depression.

However, a declining heart rate is not infrequently encountered during labor before the head becomes engaged in the lower part of the pelvis.

It has been held also that the human fetal heart rate varies with uterine contractions and relaxations.[48, 51] It is probable that a greater volume of blood is forced into the fetal heart by each uterine contraction and that the pulse rate consequently declines as the blood pressure rises in accordance with Marey's law. Clark[50] demonstrated experimentally that the fetal blood pressure undergoes a brief rise followed by a prolonged fall during contraction of the cat's uterus. He thought that the fall was due to a diminished venous return to the fetal heart which resulted from increased peripheral resistance set up in the placenta by the uterine contractions.

Although there appears to be no vagal tone before birth in sheep fetuses, ligating the umbilical cord results in an immediate elevation of the blood pressure and, in response to Marey's law, an instantaneous bradycardia. When the vagi had been cut bradycardia followed occlusion of the cord, coming on gradually or suddenly as a 2:1 heart block. In either case it appeared only after an interval of about 25 seconds during which asphyxia had developed.[51]

It has been reported that the fetal heart rate is entirely unaffected by changes in the oxygen and carbon dioxide contents of the mother's blood.[52] However, amyl nitrite, which has a great relaxing effect on uterine and other smooth muscle, has an immediate influence on the mother's heart rate and within a few seconds a similar slowing of the fetal heart occurs. This delay suggests a comparable phenomenon encountered during asphyxia in rabbit fetuses.[47]

The application of Marey's law to explain fetal bradycardia implies that vascular reflex mechanisms are functioning in the fetus, at least near term. This is not borne out by experimental evidence in all species. Observations in cat and dog fetuses at experimental Caesarean section and in the young after birth led to the conclusion that pressor reflexes make their appearance about three or four days postnatally.[46, 50] No evidence of cardio-aortic and carotid sinus reflexes was found before the fourth to sixth day in puppies and not before 11 days after birth in kittens. Faradic stimulation of the depressor and carotid sinus nerves begins to elicit reflex inhibition of the heart in 11 and 14 day old rabbits, respectively.[47] Asphyxiation fails to bring these reflexes into play until about the fortieth day of life because the blood pressure of the young animal has not attained the necessary height until this time (Fig. 7). The depressor reflex begins to be obtained when the systemic arterial pressure reaches 65 mm. Hg and the carotid sinus reflex appears at 80 mm. pressure. These are much higher pressures than are encountered in fetuses of rabbits and other small animals. In the sheep and in man at the end

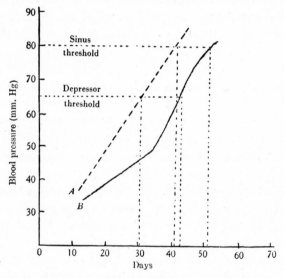

Fig. 7.—Blood pressure of rabbits at different ages after birth. *A*, Maximum blood pressure attained in asphyxia; *B*, "normal" blood pressure. (Bauer: Jour. Physiol., Vol. 95, 1939.)

of pregnancy fetal blood pressures are high enough to affect responsive cardio-aortic and carotid sinus mechanisms.

The general conclusion reached from experimental studies and clinical observations is that the fetal heart pumps blood about as fast as it can without much control by the nervous system. The vagus nerves together with their endings and central connections are capable of conduction in some species near term, but in others which are born less completely equipped to cope with their environment they may not be very well developed. Failure of cardio-inhibitory and vascular reflex mechanisms to function at birth is related at least partially to low systemic blood pressures prevailing in the smaller, less mature newborn animals. Asphyxia produces cardiac depression by direct chemical action upon the pacemaker.

An explanation of the slowing of the human fetal heart during birth may be forthcoming from these studies. It is inferred that elevation of the blood pressure caused by uterine contraction brings about a reflex bradycardia. A decline in the oxygen saturation of the fetal blood during labor may induce an anoxial cardiac depression.

The prompt but transient acceleration of the heart which occurs after breathing starts at birth may result from an awakening, as it were, of sympathetic tone consequent upon the shower of new afferent impulses from the external environment. Here too experimental evidence in the sheep is available. The smooth muscle of the fetal spleen, which is innervated by sympathetic neurons only, can be induced to contract reflexly by stimulating the central end of the cut vagus. Splenic activity also follows ligation of the umbilical cord and is not related to the changes in blood pressure occasioned by this procedure.[53] Furthermore, contraction of a smooth muscle sphincter of the ductus arteriosus occurs in the lamb at birth. In the chick sympathetic mechanisms are well formed at hatching time but vagus inhibitory function is deficient.[29]

ARTERIAL BLOOD PRESSURE

Determination of arterial blood pressure in fetuses of small animals involves difficult technical problems and one can seldom be certain that results reflect the true condition in utero. Consequently few systematic studies have been reported. The force of the embryonic chick heart at two or three days incubation can lift a column of water only two centimeters during systole.[54] Pressures of 5 mm. to 20 mm. of mercury are necessary to obliterate flow in the umbilical artery of rat fetuses 16.4 to 23.3 mm. long.[34] The variations in fetal carotid arterial pressure which accompany uterine contractions have been studied.[46, 50] Maximum estimations of 30 mm. of mercury in the cat and 40 mm. in the dog fetus were reported during the latter part of gestation. The adult level was not reached in the dog until about 40 days after birth[55] and even later in the rabbit.[47]

Haselhorst[56] has studied blood pressures in human umbilical arteries. At one Caesarean section he found it 68 mm. of mercury before delivering the child. At normal delivery in eight other experiments pressures varied between 46 mm. and 110 mm. of mercury, averaging 75 mm. It was concluded that there is no

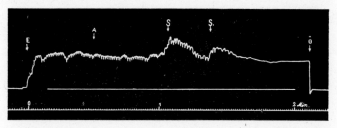

Fig. 8.—Blood pressure in the human umbilical artery at birth. Cannula inserted at *E* and withdrawn at *Ö*. Respiration began at *A* and the infant cried at *S*. (Haselhorst: Ztschr. Geburtsh. Gynäk., Vol. 95, 1929.)

significant difference between the arterial pressure at full term in utero and after delivery. An initial umbilical arterial pressure of 60 to 70 mm. of mercury was found in one newborn infant before respiration started; this did not change with the advent of respiration but was temporarily elevated to 100 mm. at the first cry. This experiment is illustrated in Fig. 8.

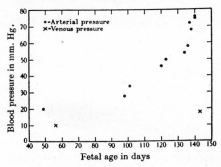

Fig. 9.—Relation between blood pressure and fetal age in the sheep. (Barcroft and Kennedy: Jour. Physiol., Vol. 95, 1939.)

Barcroft and Kennedy[57] have made the most complete series of observations correlating blood pressure with the fetal age in the sheep and their data are reproduced in Fig. 9. Other records of 39 mm. to 51 mm. of mercury at approximately 110 to 120 days gestation and 84 mm. near full term are available in this species.[58]

TABLE 6

FETAL BLOOD PRESSURE NEAR TERM

Species	Artery mm. Hg	Vein mm. Hg
Rat	20	.....
Guinea pig	......	5–10
Rabbit	20*	.....
Cat	30	7–13
Dog	40*	.....
Sheep	76– 84	18
Man	68–110	22–24

* Left ventricular systolic pressure.

A marked elevation of the blood pressure has been observed to accompany respiration at birth of the sheep.[51, 59] It is thought to be caused by respiration but not necessarily to be permanently maintained by it. How this comes about is illustrated in Fig. 10.

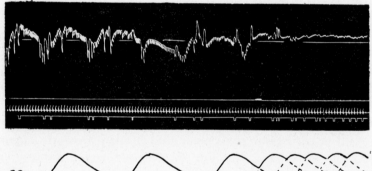

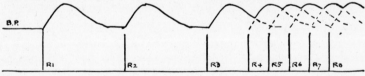

Fig. 10.—Femoral arterial blood pressure of the lamb at birth. The first and subsequent respirations are indicated by the signal (lower line); time in seconds. A diagrammatic interpretation of the effect of respirations (R$_1$, R$_2$, etc.) in elevating the blood pressure is shown below the tracing. (Barcroft: "The Brain and Its Environment," Yale Univ. Press.)

It was suggested that the cardio-accelerator center of the brain is set into activity by afferent impulses from the lungs or diaphragm. Vasoconstriction, like the contraction of the splenic smooth muscle, may be initiated similarly.

Another investigator[32] has suggested that an elevation of systemic arterial pressures and the increase in the rate of heart beat after birth are factors which operate to overcome the apnea of fetal life and initiate respiration by causing more blood of high carbon dioxide content to reach the respiratory center in the brain. But the truly significant elevation of blood pressure *follows* respiration. It is probable that any marked rise in arterial pressure appearing upon establishment of respiration signifies that the fetus was previously depressed by asphyxia. Some experiments have demonstrated prenatal arterial pressures nearly as high as those after breathing has begun.

By means of a special high-speed hypodermic manometer and photographic recording, Hamilton, Woodbury and Woods[60] have obtained left ventricular pressures of 45/2 and 50/0 in dog fetuses near term before breathing started. In the specimen having a pressure of 45/2 this increased to 50/0 after the umbilical cord had been clamped and breathing had begun. Pressures were 14/0 in a premature rabbit fetus, 20/1 at term before breathing began, 28/0 at the end of inspiration at birth and 30/3 at the end of expiration. The newborn rabbit's pressures were 30/1 at inspiration and 40/1 at expiration; those of the two day old were 27/2 and 47/11. It is evident that the left ventricular pressure rises and falls with expiration and inspiration but the mean pressure increases only gradually toward the adult level after respiration is established. Hamilton and his colleagues found that right and left ventricular pressures taken simultaneously were similar before breathing. Clamping the umbilical cord caused little or no change, but they point out that the umbilical circuit may have been obliterated before they clamped the umbilical cord. Upon establishment of air breathing the right ventricular pressure dropped in inspiration more than the left because a negative intrathoracic pressure was established, resulting in decreased peripheral resistance in the lungs.

VENOUS BLOOD PRESSURE

Several investigators have reported venous pressures taken from the fetus at experimental hysterotomy. Cohnstein and Zuntz[58] found pressures in the lamb's umbilical vein to vary between 16 mm. and 34 mm. of mercury at about 110 to 120 days gestation, and 33 mm. near term. The average of these values

was about half the average of the arterial pressures. This gave
the impression that the venous pressure of the fetus is relatively
much higher than that of the adult. Barcroft and Kennedy[57] have
estimated the pressure in the umbilical vein of the fetal sheep to
be less than 10 mm. at 56 day gestation, about 10 mm. at 110 days
and 18 mm. of mercury at 140 days (see Fig. 9). Blood passes
through the umbilical veins of cat and guinea pig fetuses near
term under pressures of 5 mm. to 13 mm. Hg, rising and falling
with contraction and relaxation of the uterine musculature.[61]
Arterial pressures were not obtained in these animals but it is
probable that they were considerably more than twice the venous
pressures. Because all the estimations of fetal venous pressures
were made at experimental hysterotomy it is probable that many
were higher than in utero, being elevated by the force exerted
upon the vascular bed of the placenta by the contracting uterus.
Actually a greater differential between systemic arterial and venous
pressures is to be expected in the undisturbed fetus in utero than
appears from the records obtained in the older experiments. It is
difficult to believe that there can be urine formation in the fetal
kidneys if the venous pressure is as much as half the arterial pressure (see Chapter VIII).

Haselhorst[56] recorded the pressure in the human umbilical
vein at Caesarean sections in three instances while the uterus was
quiescent. It varied between 22 and 34 mm. of mercury. In one
case the pressure in the vein increased from 24 to 70 mm. when
pituitrin was injected into the uterus. A possible placental or
uterine function in maintaining an adequate venous return to the
fetus should not be overlooked.

REFERENCES CITED

1. Fano, G. 1885. Lo Sperimentale, 1: 143 (cited by F. Bottazzi & G.
   Fano, 1900, in Richet's Dict. Physiol., 4: 253, Alcan, Paris).
2. Hooker, D. 1911. J. Exp. Zool., 11: 159.
3. Lillie, F. R. 1919. The Development of the Chick, Henry Holt, N. Y.
4. Sabin, F. R. 1920. Contrib. Emb., 9: 213.
5. Johnstone, P. N. 1925. Johns Hopkins Hosp. Bull., 36: 299.
6. Patten, B. M. & T. C. Kramer. 1933. Am. J. Anat., 53: 349.
7. Goss, C. M. 1938. Anat. Rec., 70: 505.
8. Copenhaver, W. M. 1939. J. Exp. Zool., 80: 193.
9. Fano, G. & F. Bodano. 1890. Arch. Ital. Biol., 13: 387.
10. Pickering, J. W. 1893. J. Physiol., 14: 383.

11. Paff, G. H. 1935. Anat. Rec., 63: 203.
12. Cremer, M. 1906. Münch. med. Wochenschr., 1: 811.
13. Foà, C. 1911. Arch. Ital. Biol., 56: 145.
14. Nörr, J. 1921. Ztschr. Biol., 73: 123.
15. Sachs, H. 1923. Pflüger's Arch., 197: 536.
16. Haynal, E. & D. Kellner. 1924. Ztschr. klin. Med., 98: 365.
17. Maekawa, M. & J. Toyoshima. 1930. Acta Sch. Med. Univ. Imp. Kyoto, 12: 519.
18. Strassmann, E. O. 1936. Staff Proc. Mayo Clin., 11: 778.
19. Bell, G. H. 1938. J. Obst. Gyn. Brit. Emp., 45: 802.
20. Steffan, H. & E. Strassmann. 1933. Zentralbl. Gynäk., 57: 610.
21. Krumbhaar, E. B. 1916. Am. J. Physiol., 40: 133.
22. Easby, M. H. 1934. Am. Heart J., 10: 118.
23. Heard, J. D., G. G. Burkley & C. R. Schaefer. 1936. Am. Heart J., 11: 41.
24. Krumbhaar, E. B. & H. H. Jenks. 1917. Heart, 6: 189.
25. Lewis, T. 1916. Phil. Trans. Roy. Soc., Lond. B., 207: 221.
26. Patten, B. M. 1933. In A. H. Curtis' Obstetrics and Gynecology, 1: 906, Saunders, Philadelphia.
27. Bogue, I. Y. 1933. J. Exp. Biol., 10: 286.
28. Hoff, E. C., T. C. Kramer, D. DuBois & B. M. Patten. 1939. Amer. Heart J., 17: 470.
29. Cohn, A. E. & E. L. Wile. 1925. J. Exp. Med., 42: 291.
30. Bogue, I. Y. 1933. J. Exp. Biol., 9: 351.
31. Blackfan, K. D. 1932. Growth and Development of the Child; White House Conference Reports. Sect. I, Pt. 1: p. 53. Century Co., N. Y.
32. Krafka, J. 1933. Am. J. Dis. Child., 45: 1007.
33. Sontag, L. W. and T. W. Richards. 1938. Monog. Soc. Res. Child Devel., Vol. 3, No. 4.
34. Corey, E. L. 1932. Am. J. Physiol., 101: 304.
35. Hartman, C. G., R. R. Squier & O. L. Tinklepaugh. 1930. Proc. Soc. Exp. Biol. & Med., 28: 285.
36. Barcroft, J. 1936. Physiol. Rev., 16: 103.
37. Clark, A. J. 1927. Comparative Physiology of the Heart, Cambridge Univ. Press.
38. Bottazzi, F. & G. Fano. 1900. In C. Richet's Dictionnaire de Physiologie, 4: 253, Alcan, Paris.
39. Pickering, J. W. 1896. J. Physiol., 20: 165.
40. Soltmann, O. 1877. Jahrb. Kinderhlk., 11: 101.
41. Anrep, B. 1880. Pflüger's Arch., 21: 78.
42. Heinricius, G. 1890. Ztschr. Biol., 26: 197.
43. Meyer, E. 1893. Arch. Physiol. Norm. et Path., 5: 475.
44. Buglia, G. 1926. Arch. Fisiol., 24: 448.
45. Kellogg, H. B. 1927. Proc. Soc. Exp. Biol. & Med., 24: 839.
46. Clark, G. A. 1934. J. Physiol., 83: 229.
47. Bauer, D. J. 1938. Ibid., 93: 90; 95: 187.
48. Leff, M. 1932. Am. J. Obst. Gyn., 24: 898.
49. Wiggers, C. J. 1924. In I. A. Abt's Pediatrics, 4: 198, Saunders, Philadelphia.
50. Clark, G. A. 1932. J. Physiol., 74: 391.

51. Barcroft, J.   1938.   The Brain and Its Environment.   Yale Univ. Press, New Haven.
52. Rech, W.   1931.   Arch. Gynäk., 147: 82.
53. Taylor, D. B. & T. Gotsev.   1938.   Cited by J. Barcroft, 1938.
54. Hill, L. & Y. Azuma.   1927.   J. Physiol., 62: 27P.
55. Clark, G. A. & H. E. Holling.   1931.   Ibid., 73: 305.
56. Haselhorst, G.   1929.   Ztschr. Geburtsh. Gynäk., 95: 400.
57. Barcroft, J. & J. A. Kennedy.   1939.   J. Physiol., 95: 173.
58. Cohnstein, J. & N. Zuntz.   1884.   Pflüger's Arch., 34: 173.
59. Cohnstein, J. & N. Zuntz.   1888.   Ibid., 42: 342.
60. Hamilton, W. F., R. A. Woodbury & E. B. Woods.   1937.   Am. J. Physiol., 119: 206.
61. DeMarsh, Q. B. & W. F. Windle.   1939.   Unpublished.

CHAPTER III

THE FETAL CIRCULATION

VOLUME OF BLOOD AND RATE OF CIRCULATION

BLOOD volume is usually expressed as a function of body surface or body weight in the adult. The fetus has no surface from which heat is lost and therefore it is illogical to use surface relationships in indicating its blood volume. If we are to express it in terms of the weight of fetal tissues through which the blood passes we must consider not only the weight of the fetus itself but also that of the placenta. The relationship between the two changes greatly as gestation proceeds.

The blood volume of five human infants 2½ to 8 hours after birth was found to vary between 144 and 173 cc. per kilogram body weight, averaging 156.4 cc. per kilogram,[1] but no data are available for human fetuses. The amount of fetal blood in the placenta is not known; but 100 cc. or more can be recovered from the placenta when the umbilical cord is clamped immediately after birth. Much of this blood will return to the fetus if clamping is delayed.

Determinations of blood volume have been made by Cohnstein and Zuntz[2] in rabbits and by Elliott, Hall and Huggett[3] in goats.

TABLE 7
BLOOD VOLUME IN GOAT FETUSES

Fetal age	Total blood volume	Blood volume in fetus	Total volume of blood
		$\dfrac{cc. \times 100}{wt. \ in \ grams}$	$\dfrac{cc. \times 100}{wt. \ in \ grams}$
days	cc.		
68	16.3	21.8	8.0
71	40.4	40.4	8.8
77	39.9	23.9	8.6
85	64.0	23.0	8.6
101	112.0	17.3	9.5
113	145.0	11.6	6.8
126	204.0	14.2	9.9
136	136.0*	14.2	9.6
144	428.0	14.7	11.95

* Triplet.

The latter investigators used the method of injecting a known amount of dye into the fetal vessels and estimating its dilution in the blood stream.   Their results are summarized in Table 7.[9] More recently Barcroft and Kennedy[4] have employed an improved colorimetric dye injection method (Evan's Blue, T 1,824) to study blood volume in sheep fetuses from the standpoint of development.   Their results are illustrated in Figs. 11 and 12.

The placental cotyledons of the sheep reach maximal weight at about the middle of gestation when the fetus weighs only about

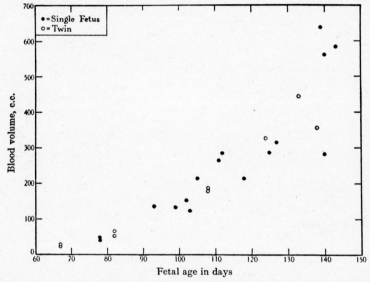

Fig. 11.—The relation of blood volume in the fetus + the placenta to age in single fetuses (●) and twin fetuses (o).   (Barcroft and Kennedy: Jour. Physiol., Vol. 95, 1939.)

200 grams.   It is evident that the blood forms a much larger part of the fetal body weight at this time than it does toward full term. The absolute amount of blood increases greatly in the fetal body but that in the placenta remains nearly constant throughout the last third of gestation.   At 100 days of gestation the fetal blood is divided about equally between fetal body and placenta; at approximately full term only about one-fourth of it is in the placenta. Twin fetuses weigh a little less than single fetuses of comparable age, and their volume of blood is even less than encountered in single fetuses of comparable weight.

Although the amount of blood in the uterus at any one time during the last quarter of gestation remains about the same, the quantity traversing the uterus per minute more than doubles between 110 and 140 days. This may be related to the increase in fetal blood pressure (see Chapter II). The rate of blood flow to and from the placenta is surprisingly great in the last quarter of fetal life.[5] At 111 days of gestation 111 cc. of blood traversed the umbilical vessels per minute, and at 137 days this had increased to 568 cc. per minute. Similarly on the maternal side in the same

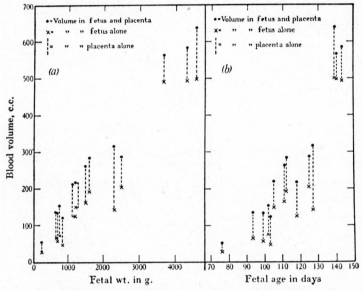

Fig. 12.—The blood volume in relation to (a) fetal weight and (b) fetal age in single fetuses. (Barcroft and Kennedy: Jour. Physiol., Vol. 95, 1939.)

animals the rates of flow were 106 cc. per minute and 475 cc. per minute. Lower values were obtained at full term, and the significance of this is not clear; contraction of the uterus upon the placenta may have impeded the flow. Table 8 contains the data which have been reported.

The time taken for blood to circulate from the umbilical vein through the body of the human fetus and back to the umbilical artery has been estimated.[6] The mean circulation time before birth was found to be 30 seconds, and after birth, 60 seconds.

The cardiac output of the heart has been estimated in the

sheep fetus,[7-9] but in view of the surprisingly rapid flow through the umbilical circuit it must be considerably greater than was reported in the earlier studies. More information is needed on this question.

TABLE 8

RATE OF BLOOD FLOW THROUGH THE PLACENTA IN THE SHEEP

Age of fetus (days)	Wt. of fetus (grams)	Blood vol. (cc.) of fetus	Rate of blood flow	
			Umbilical cord cc./min.	Uterus cc./min.
111	1,200	125	111	106
126	3,000	270	218	161
127	2,850	265	162	179
129	2,750	270	600	...
137	3,850	350	568	475
138	3,650	360	284	347
152	2,800	412	300	268

THE COURSE OF THE FETAL BLOOD

The course of the blood through the fetal heart has been the subject of controversy for more than a century. Most of the arguments need not be considered in this place, for readers who are interested in the historical aspects of this subject can consult the excellent review of Pohlman.[10] Three principal theories are supported by experimental observations.

The one which has been favored by most writers until a few years ago holds that oxygenated blood from the placenta is brought by way of the umbilical vein, ductus venosus (part going through liver sinuses) and inferior vena cava to the right atrium of the fetal heart. A fold of endocardium known as the valve of the inferior vena cava directs this stream of more richly oxygenated blood across the blood filled right atrium and through the foramen ovale into the left atrium. Pulmonary venous blood, said to be negligible in quantity before birth, is added to it there. This still relatively well oxygenated mixture of blood enters the left ventricle, is pumped into the ascending aorta and the arch from which spring the great vessels supplying the heart, head and upper extremities. A small quantity passes on through the aortic isthmus into the descending aorta. Venous blood returning from the rostral parts of the body by way of the superior vena cava enters the right atrium and is said to cross the stream from the inferior vena cava without mixing with it. This reduced blood passes into the right ventricle which forces it into the pulmonary arterial trunk; a little goes to the lungs but the greater part is shunted by the ductus arteriosus connecting the pulmonary artery with that part of the aorta distal to its great branches. There a smaller volume of the more highly oxygenated blood from the left side of the heart joins it and passes to the lower extremities as well as back to the placenta by way of the hypogastric and umbilical arteries. This is the Sabatier (1791) doctrine, supported originally only by anatomical observations.

Opposed to it is the theory developed by Pohlman[10] and Kellogg[11, 12] which holds that two streams of fluid entering a common chamber from opposite directions must mix. Accordingly, the well oxygenated umbilical vein blood, diluted once when joined by venous blood of the abdominal inferior vena cava, enters the right atrium and is diluted again by that arriving from the upper part of the body in the superior vena cava. The resulting complete mixture goes two ways. Part passes into the right ventricle through the right atrio-ventricular orifice; the remainder traverses the foramen ovale and left atrium to enter the left ventricle. According to this view the aortic and the pulmonary ductus arteriosus streams of blood are approximately alike in respect to oxygen content, and the upper parts of the body, including the heart which is the only organ working as hard in fetal life as it does in the newborn, receive no better blood than do the trunk, inferior extremities and placenta. It is assumed that no significant quantity of blood enters the fetal heart by channels other than the two venae cavae.

Let us defer consideration of the third hypothesis for the moment and examine the experimental evidence in favor of the Sabatier and Pohlman-Kellogg theories. The first study was made more than a century ago[13] by injecting pastes of contrasting color into the superior and inferior venae cavae of three dead human fetuses under equal pressures. In one fetus the injection of the superior vena cava failed to reach the heart, in one the two colored masses underwent some mixing, and in the third, a fetus of seven months, the two crossed without mixing. The experiment was accepted as a demonstration of the validity of the Sabatier theory.

Direct observation of the beating heart of guinea pig fetuses whose placental circulation was intact has shown that the two sides differ in color, the left being bright and the right being dark.[9] Similarly in cat fetuses we have observed that when the umbilical vein blood is brilliantly red the carotid artery sometimes appears bright and the umbilical artery dull. There are certain objections to accepting such observations as these favoring the Sabatier doctrine, however. The left ventricle of the fetal heart has a thinner wall than the right and may appear brighter even though the oxygen content of the blood is the same in both chambers. The bright red color of the umbilical vein of the cat fetus often results from contraction of the uterus which sends blood to the heart under higher pressures than are normally encountered. When the intra-uterine pressure is unevenly distributed in a fetus which has been removed from the uterus, oxygenated blood may surge through the foramen ovale and into the left side of the heart in unusual proportions.

Experiments lending support to the second view, that the two caval blood streams mix completely in the right atrium, were initiated by Pohlman[10, 14] who was the first investigator to use living fetuses in a study of the course of blood before birth. He determined that both ventricles of the fetal pig heart have nearly equal capacities and that the ventricular pressures are practically identical. A saline suspension of corn starch was injected into the umbilical vein or into the fetal superior vena cava. Thereafter equal quantities of starch were recovered from samples of blood withdrawn from the two ventricles.

Kellogg[11] repeated and extended these experiments, using a much larger series of pig fetuses. He demonstrated that material injected into either the umbilical vein or the fetal superior vena cava appeared at the same instant in both ventricles. After simultaneously withdrawing equal samples under the same pressure from the two ventricles equal numbers of starch grains per cc. were counted in each sample. Sedimentation of starch from larger volumes of blood taken from the two ventricles confirmed these observations. Similar results have been obtained in chick embryos.[15]

It was thought that injection of a foreign substance may have blocked capillary beds beyond the heart, resulted in stasis and consequent churning of the blood within the heart. Therefore, Kellogg[12] resorted to direct manometric gas analyses of small ventricular blood samples. For this investigation dog fetuses were delivered under local anesthesia, care being taken to maintain the placental circulation intact. It proved impossible to obtain adequate samples from the two ventricles simultaneously in the dog without collapsing the heart. Consequently blood was first withdrawn from one ventricle, then after a few minutes, from the other. The order of taking was alternated. Sixteen samples from each ventricle were analyzed. The average values obtained from right and left ventricular blood were 2.38 and 2.43 volumes per cent of oxygen and 44.33 and 42.69 volumes per cent of carbon dioxide. These data seemed to indicate that the two caval streams of the dog fetus undergo rather thorough mixing in the right atrium of the heart, assuming that the fetal pulmonary veins added a negligible quantity of blood to the left atrium. It will be shown presently however that the pulmonary return is much greater than was previously supposed. Therefore the studies under discussion do not prove complete mixture in the right atrium.

Other studies in goat and sheep fetuses by Huggett[16] and Barcroft[9] seem to indicate that the blood takes a figure of eight course through the fetal body, first through an "upper" circulation and then through a "lower," but without complete mixture in the right atrium. The evidence is based on a comparison of values obtained by determining oxygen content of the blood drawn from upper and lower circulations, e.g., from the carotid and umbilical arteries of the fetuses. The data in question are reproduced in Table 9. More recently additional blood-gas analyses have be-

TABLE 9

OXYGEN CONTENT OF BLOOD IN THE UPPER AND LOWER FETAL CIRCULATIONS

Goat no.	Umbilical vein (vol. %)	Carotid artery (vol. %)	Umbilical artery (vol. %)	Sheep no.	Umbilical vein (vol. %)	Carotid artery (vol. %)	Umbilical artery (vol. %)
B.....	7.0	6.0	6.0	11.....	11.3–12.3	10.3	6.9–9.2
C.....	6.5	4.2	0.25	14.....	15.7	10.4	10.4
D.....	5.0	4.5	0.9	16.....	17.4	9.1	5.2
M.....	12.0	9.0	4.0	19.....	6.8	3.7	1.7
N.....	9.7	4.7	3.0	27.....	10.5	6.9	5.9
O.....	7.5	7.0	3.5				
Ave....	7.96	5.9	2.94	Ave....	12.3–12.4	8.3	6.0–6.3

come available in sheep fetuses[17] and these are included in Fig. 13. The data lend considerable support to the classical Sabatier theory but do not prove that a complete crossing of the streams occurs in the right atrium.

All data based upon fetal blood-gas analysis are open to criticism. No one can doubt that physiologic conditions are upset when fetuses are removed from the uterus. Even though the placentas were left intact the uterine-placental relationships were altered and various degrees of anoxemia were set up in the fetuses.

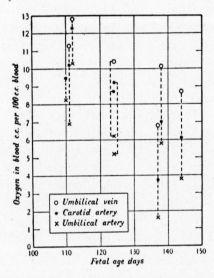

Fig. 13.—Comparison of the oxygen content of blood from the umbilical vein (o), carotid artery (•) and umbilical artery (x) at different fetal ages (sheep). (Barcroft: "The Brain and Its Environment," Yale Univ. Press.)

It is difficult to believe that the blood of the fetal heart contains as little oxygen as was encountered in the dog at Caesarean section, and it is even questionable if a proportional reduction could have taken place in the two ventricular samples. The withdrawal of blood from only one ventricle at a time may have disturbed pressures and have led to serious errors.

The blood-gas analyses in goats and sheep are not quite as convincing when all the data are scrutinized as they appear on superficial inspection. In one of the experimental animals (sheep No. 11) the thoracic inferior vena cava blood appeared to contain less oxygen than that of the carotid artery, which of course is quite impossible; two different values were given for the blood of the umbilical artery, one of which was not a great deal less than that for the carotid artery. In other animals (sheep No. 14 and goat B) the carotid and umbilical artery blood contained identical amounts of oxygen.

Apparently no one has been able to obtain blood samples simultaneously from the upper and lower circulations. When this has been done the results will have more meaning than those available today. It should be pointed out that the oxygen content

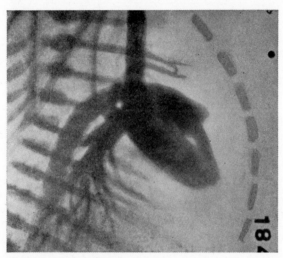

Fig. 14.—Roentgenogram showing injection of thorotrast into the superior vena cava of a living sheep fetus. The passage of blood through the right side of the heart, into the pulmonary arteries, ductus arteriosus and descending aorta may be seen. (Barclay, et al.: Brit. J. Radiol., Vol. 12, 1939.)

of the umbilical vein blood of cat fetuses near birth fluctuates widely from moment to moment and this appears to be related to rhythmical uterine contractions.[18] The inconsistencies in existing data may be related to this phenomenon. That species differences may exist must not be overlooked. Perhaps less mixing takes place in the sheep and goat than in the pig and dog fetuses, as Patten has suggested.[9]

One of the most significant studies of the fetal circulation is that of Barclay and his colleagues.[19] By means of x-ray cinephotography during injections of radio-opaque substances into the

jugular or umbilical veins of sheep fetuses they were able to follow the course of the two vena caval streams very clearly. The
superior vena cava blood appeared to pass directly through the
right atrium into the right ventricle (Fig. 14) as it should according to the Sabatier theory. The blood from the inferior vena
cava took two courses. Most of it traversed the right atrium and
foramen ovale to the left atrium and left ventricle; a small part of
it passed directly into the right ventricle (Fig. 15). Barring the
possibility that the force of injection added sufficient impetus to

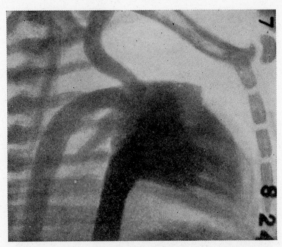

Fig. 15.—Roentgenogram showing injection of thorotrast into the inferior vena
cava of a living sheep fetus. The passage of blood through the right atrium,
foramen ovale and left side of the heart may be seen. Its course through the
brachiocephalic artery and aorta is shown. A small amount of blood enters the
right ventricle and may be seen in the pulmonary arteries. (Barclay, et al.: Brit.
J. Radiol., Vol. 12, 1939.)

the blood to overcome a normal tendency to mix in the right
atrium, these experiments prove that a very significant proportion
of the more highly oxygenated blood from the placenta goes directly to the left side of the heart of the sheep fetus to be delivered,
after mixing with reduced pulmonary blood, to the heart, upper
extremities and head. This is precisely the arrangement proposed
by Wolff[20] more than 160 years ago and supported by experiments
in dead fetuses by Ziegenspeck.[21]

Patten and Toulmin[22] have approached the question of blood
flow through the heart from an entirely different standpoint.

After determining that the average weights of the left and right ventricles are 7.11 and 8.05 grams, they measured the functional areas of all the heart apertures in 20 normal human still-born fetuses at term. Their results expressed in average diameters and areas are illustrated diagrammatically in Fig. 16. Although they point out that it would be unwise to draw too specific conclusions about the circulation merely from the sizes of vessels, they are in-

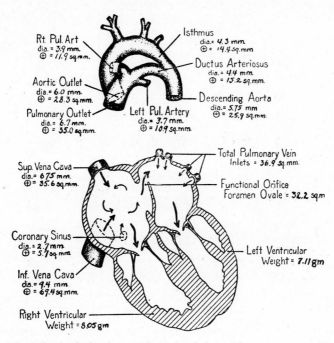

Fig. 16.—Dimensions of the human heart and its orifices at term. (Patten & Toulmin: White House Conference Reports, D. Appleton-Century Co.)

clined to believe that their results demonstrate a mechanism unfavorable to the classical Sabatier theory.

Since left and right ventricular pressures are equal in the fetal heart,[23] the $\frac{\text{right ventricular weight}}{\text{left ventricular weight}}$ should equal $\frac{\text{area of pulmonary outlet}}{\text{area of aortic outlet}}$. From their data, $\frac{8.05}{7.11}$ should equal $\frac{35.0}{28.9}$. The ratios are actually in the proportion of 0.938 to 1. If the volume of blood entering the atria is proportional to the size of the inlets the following proposition should be true:

Entering right atrium   *Entering left atrium*

Superior vena cava..   35.6 sq. mm.
Inferior vena cava...   69.7 sq. mm.
Coronary sinus.....   5.7 sq. mm.

Total....... 111.0 sq. mm.   Total pulmonary veins......... 36.9 sq. mm.
            − 32.2 sq. mm.→ Functional orifice of foramen ovale. 32.2 sq. mm.

Net.........   78.8 sq. mm.   Total................... 69.1 sq. mm.
Entering right ventricle   *Entering left ventricle*

If these figures are functionally significant the ratio of blood received by the two ventricles should equal both the ratio of right ventricular to left ventricular weights and the ratio of pulmonary to aortic outlet areas. Substituting figures obtained from heart measurements:

$\frac{78.8}{69.1}$ should equal $\frac{8.05}{7.11}$ or 1.1404 should equal 1.1307, which is in agreement in ratio of 0.989 to 1.

$\frac{78.8}{69.1}$ should equal $\frac{35.0}{28.9}$ or 1.1404 should equal 1.2111, which is in agreement in ratio of 0.941 to 1.

"Tentatively then," they conclude, "a ratio of about 8 to 7 may be accepted as expressing the relations between right and left divisions of the fetal heart."

It is generally assumed that the prenatal lungs, requiring but a very small amount of blood for their own metabolism, are supplied with a negligible quantity until the moment of birth when they expand and take over respiratory function. At that time a radical rerouting of the blood is supposed to take place with dramatic suddenness. This conception has been questioned by Patten and his colleagues.[22, 24-26] In normal still-born human hearts they found the average combined cross-sectional area of the pulmonary arteries to be 22.8 sq. mm. and that of the pulmonary veins, 36.9 sq. mm. The functional orifice of the foramen ovale was only 32.2 sq. mm. Comparison of the pulmonary vessel measurements with others from newborns which had died after breathing showed them to have virtually the same capacity. The total cross-sectional area of the pulmonary veins was found to be about the same as that of the umbilical vein. The combined area of the left and right pulmonary arteries about equals that of the umbilical arteries.

The orifice of the foramen ovale is so restricted by attachments of its flap-like valve in late fetal life that it alone can not be assumed to deliver enough blood to the left atrium to bring about an equalization of pressure there with that in the right atrium. And yet it has been proved that the two ventricular pressures are practically equal in the fetus before breathing starts.[10, 23] Although it is reasonable to assume from these facts that pulmonary venous return makes up the difference the evidence from the starch experiments casts doubt upon the theory,[10, 11] for if there is complete mixing in the right atrium and if there is a significant volume of blood returning from the fetal lungs to dilute the starch laden blood from the foramen ovale less starch should have been recovered from the left ventricle than from the right.

An attempt to settle the question of fetal pulmonary circulation has been made by comparing the total iron content of apneic fetal lungs with that of the lungs of litter-mate kittens which had been allowed to breathe air for an hour or more after clamping the umbilical cord.[27] The average data from nine experiments are presented in Table 10. If we can assume that the surgical pro-

TABLE 10

COMPARISON OF THE TOTAL PULMONARY IRON AND ESTIMATED PULMONARY BLOOD IN CAT FETUSES AND THEIR AIR BREATHING LITTER MATES

	No. of speci- mens	Total iron (mgs.)	Mgs. Fe per gm. ashed lung	Total Hb.* (gms.)	Gms. Hb.* per gm. ashed lung	Estimated blood volume*	
						Total in lungs (cc.)	Per gm. ashed lung (cc.)
No air...	12	0.322	5.695	0.0959	1.698	0.9036	15.546
Breathed.	15	0.3195	5.938	0.0951	1.782	0.8690	15.527

* Assuming all iron to be in hemoglobin of blood; amount of tissue iron is unknown but would be equal in the two series.

cedures involved in the experiments did not destroy a real difference between the apneic fetuses and the air breathing kittens it is quite evident from Table 10 that a circulation must be present in the lungs during late prenatal life which is wholly capable of caring for oxygenation pending the assumption of respiration, and that there is no sudden increase in its volume.

Direct observation of the fetal lungs before and after breathing lends support to this view; the apneic fetal lungs present the appearance of highly vascular organs. It has been estimated that more than five per cent of the fetal blood is in the human lungs before breathing begins.[28] Furthermore the recent studies of Barclay and his colleagues[19] in the sheep fetus have demonstrated radiographically that the pulmonary arteries and veins carry a very appreciable volume of blood. Perhaps the crucial evidence favoring the concept of a significant pulmonary blood volume before birth is that afforded by the exceedingly rare condition, congenital stenosis of the pulmonary veins, in which the left ventricle develops only about half its normal capacity and muscular power.[26] It seems probable that Patten's original anatomical study portrays the true state of the pulmonary circulation before birth.

Correlation of the various studies just discussed leaves us with rather a different conception of the fetal circulation than is expressed by either of the two prevalent theories, although it must be granted that there are points for disputation on both sides. In the first place, one is justified in assuming some mixture of the two caval streams in the right atrium, at least in respect to the blood which goes to the right ventricle. Secondly, there can be little doubt that a greater quantity of the highly oxygenated blood from the placenta enters the left atrium than finds its way into the right ventricle. Knowing that the fetal pulmonary veins return a stream of blood to the left side of the heart approximately as large as that of the umbilical vein, we fail to see how complete mixing would have taken place[10, 11] in the right atrium and as much starch have been recovered from the left ventricle as from the right. More than half of the inferior caval blood must have traversed the foramen ovale. As a matter of fact Kellogg[11] did recover more starch from the left ventricle in each of five dog fetuses of one series in which all the injections had been made into the umbilical veins. If there is a complete mixture of the two caval streams in the right atrium and if there is any loss of oxygen in the pulmonary circuit the lower half of the fetal body must receive more highly oxygenated blood than the heart and brain.

Perhaps after all the long discarded concept of Wolff and Ziegenspeck, which held that the superior vena cava blood goes entirely to the right ventricle but that the inferior caval stream passes to both left and right sides, is more nearly correct than either of the more prevalent theories of fetal circulation even though the methods originally used to arrive at this conclusion were not exactly physiologic. It is this theory that the observa-

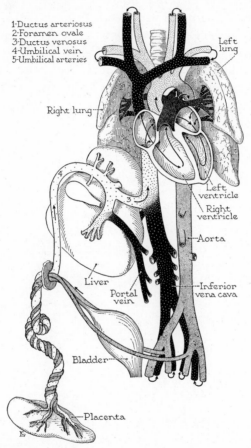

1-Ductus arteriosus
2-Foramen ovale
3-Ductus venosus
4-Umbilical vein
5-Umbilical arteries

Left lung

Right lung

Left ventricle

Right ventricle

Aorta

Liver

Portal vein

Inferior vena cava

Bladder

Placenta

Fig. 17.—The fetal circulation and probable course of the blood through the fetal heart. The most highly oxygenated blood is contained in the vessels least shaded, the most completely reduced blood, in the darkest vessels, and four intermediate degrees of reduction due to mixing are indicated by four intermediate shades.

tions of Barcroft, Barclay and their colleagues support. The concept is illustrated in Fig. 17.

Again, a word of caution. There is no reason to believe that the same conditions are met in all species. It is quite possible that a greater proportion of the blood from the placenta reaches the left side of the heart without dilution in the sheep fetus than in man.*

CHANGES IN THE CIRCULATION AT BIRTH

Occlusion of the placental circulation is the most immediate event at birth. The umbilical arteries continue to pulsate for a few moments but very soon they constrict, allowing no more blood to leave the body of the newborn. Much of the blood which is in the placenta drains back into the newborn if the umbilical cord is not clamped immediately.[29] It has been estimated on the basis of 120 averaged cases that about 50 grams of blood returns to the child in the first minute and 98 grams by the thirtieth minute after birth.[30]

It may be suggested that there is a reduction in the amount of blood entering the right atrium when the umbilical vessels are occluded. It is unsound to assume that development in fetal life has given the child an abdominal vena cava larger than necessary for the prenatal blood flow. This vessel probably does not accommodate immediately to the increased load placed upon it by obliteration of the umbilical arteries, but only gradually increases in diameter as postnatal growth takes place. What happens to the extra blood? We may surmise that the capillary bed of the newborn opens to receive more blood. This seems reasonable in view of the increased muscular work and initiation of new activities, including tonus.

Less blood enters the right atrium and its filling pressure consequently decreases. Hamilton and his colleagues[23] found no appreciable difference between intraventricular pressures before and after clamping the umbilical cord, but they suggested that the umbilical circuit may have been shut off before their observations were made. If the filling pressures of the two sides of the heart are about equal after the umbilical cord has been occluded any fall on the right side or any rise on the left will cause the valve of the foramen ovale to close. In the dog and the rabbit another flap-like valve guards the opening of the ductus arteriosus into the

* Some recently completed injection experiments in living cat and guinea-pig fetuses provide a striking demonstration of the crossing of the caval streams. They appear to support the Sabatier doctrine even more completely than do Barclay's studies.

aorta; this too will close. With inspiration at birth in the dog and rabbit a negative intrathoracic pressure brings about a direct fall in pressure on both sides of the heart followed by a rise to the original level with expiration. As the negative intrathoracic pressure becomes permanently established it is thought to lead to a decrease in the peripheral resistance within the blood channels of the lungs, but of course not in the systemic capillaries; consequently the right intraventricular systolic pressure declines more than does the left which increases with development of systemic vasomotor tonus. The diastolic pressures remain about equal during the early hours after birth, but by two days in the rabbit diastolic pressures are considerably higher on the left side than on the right. As soon as the peripheral resistance is lowered, we may assume an increased blood flow through the lungs with increased filling pressure of the left atrium which renders the valve of the foramen ovale permanently closed from a functional standpoint.

There is reason to believe that the events occurring at birth vary in the different species. In the sheep we know nothing about intraventricular pressures but other information is at hand.[17] When the umbilical cord is clamped there is a brief transient rise in blood pressure followed by the establishment of respiration. When breathing becomes regular the mean systemic blood pressure reaches a higher level than it had before respiration began. Development of sympathetic vaso-pressor tonus has been suggested to take place concomitant with establishment of respiration. It is known that the splenic smooth muscle begins to contract at that time and, more important, the ductus arteriosus closes by sphincter action.[17, 31]* These events seem to indicate that provision is made for the right side of the heart to function at lower pressure levels than the left in the newborn lamb.

What are the conditions in man? Here we are faced with inadequate data. It has been held that the systemic blood pressure does not change significantly with the advent of respiration at birth.[32] The ductus arteriosus possesses no valve like that of the rabbit and dog; nor has it been shown to occlude immediately

---

* Barclay and his colleagues[19] have found recently that they were mistaken about the identity of the ductus arteriosus in their first study. Nevertheless I am convinced, from direct observations in Professor Barcroft's laboratory, that the ductus does occlude within a few minutes after breathing starts.

by sphincter action like that of the lamb. Its closure is said to be accomplished very gradually over a period of several weeks or months by a process resembling that encountered in endarteritis obliterans.[26, 33-35] Intimal pads are present in the vessel during late fetal life.[35] If the ductus arteriosus remains open after birth it must be assumed that pressures on the two sides of the heart will tend to equalize and that blood can flow from the aorta into the pulmonary artery. One should expect to hear the character-

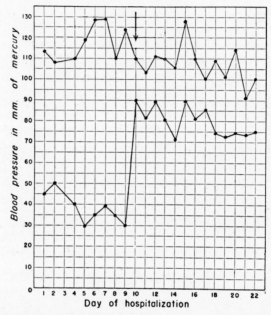

Fig. 18.—Daily blood pressures (upper: systolic; lower: diastolic) before and after ligating a patent ductus arteriosus in a 7 year old child. Day of operation indicated by the arrow. (Gross and Hubbard: J.A.M.A., Vol. 112, 1939.)

istic murmur of a patent ductus in every infant, but this is not the case. It would seem that there must be some mechanism as yet undiscovered in the human to bring about functional closure of the ductus arteriosus at birth. It is common to find an anatomically patent ductus at autopsy in early life, but it is questionable if postmortem ductus arteriosus patency soon after birth can be taken as proof of a true physiologic patency existing before death. Continued patency of the ductus arteriosus several years after birth is a relatively common occurrence. But the condition predisposes toward bacterial endocarditis and is in itself a danger because of the additional load placed upon the left ventricle which may lead to cardiac decompensation. Successful surgical ligation of a patent ductus arteriosus in a 7 year old child has been reported recently.[36] The effects of this operation upon the diastolic blood pressure are shown in Fig. 18.

REFERENCES CITED

1. Lucas, W. P. & B. F. Dearing. 1921. Am. J. Dis. Child., 21: 96.
2. Cohnstein, J. & N. Zuntz. 1888. Pflüger's Arch., 42: 342.
3. Elliott, R. H., F. G. Hall, & A. St. G. Huggett. 1934. J. Physiol., 82: 160.
4. Barcroft, J. & J. A. Kennedy. 1939. Ibid., 95: 173.
5. Barcroft, J., J. A. Kennedy & M. F. Mason. 1939. Ibid., 95: 269.
6. Haselhorst, G. & K. Stromberger. 1932. Ztschr. Geburtsh. Gynäk., 102: 16.
7. Cohnstein, J. & N. Zuntz. 1884. Pflüger's Arch., 34: 173.
8. Barcroft, J., L. B. Flexner, T. McCurkin. 1934. J. Physiol., 82: 498.
9. Barcroft, J. 1936. Physiol. Rev., 16: 103.
10. Pohlman, A. G. 1909. Anat. Rec., 3: 75.
11. Kellogg, H. B. 1928. Am. J. Anat., 42: 443.
12. Kellogg, H. B. 1930. Am. J. Physiol., 91: 637.
13. Reid, J. 1835. Edin. Med. Surg. J., 43: 11; 308.
14. Pohlman, A. G. 1907. Johns Hopkins Hosp. Bull., 18: 409.
15. Magruder, S. R. 1932. Anat. Rec., 54: 137.
16. Huggett, A. St. G. 1927. J. Physiol., 62: 373.
17. Barcroft, J. 1938. The Brain and Its Environment, Yale Univ. Press, New Haven.
18. Windle, W. F. & A. G. Steele. 1938. Proc. Soc. Exper. Biol. & Med., 39: 246.
19. Barclay, A. E., J. Barcroft, D. H. Barron & K. J. Franklin. 1939. Brit. J. Radiol., 12: 505.
20. Wolff, C. F. 1778. Cited by Pohlman, 1909.
21. Ziegenspeck, R. 1882. Cited by Pohlman, 1909.
22. Patten, B. M. & K. Toulmin. 1932. Cited by K. D. Blackfan, Growth and Development of the Child; White House Conference Reports, Sect. I, Vol. 2, p. 262. Century Co., N. Y.
23. Hamilton, W. F., R. A. Woodbury & E. B. Woods. 1937. Am. J. Physiol., 119: 206.
24. Patten, B. M., W. A. Sommerfield & G. H. Paff. 1929. Anat. Rec., 44: 165.
25. Patten, B. M. 1931. Am. J. Anat., 48: 19.
26. Patten, B. M. 1933. In A. H. Curtis' Obstetrics and Gynecology, 1: 906, Saunders, Philadelphia.
27. Abel, S. & W. F. Windle. 1939. Anat. Rec., 75: 451.
28. Krafka, J. 1933. Am. J. Dis. Child., 45: 1007.
29. Frischkorn, H. B. & M. P. Rucker. 1939. Am. J. Obst. Gyn., 38: 592.
30. Haselhorst, G. & A. Allmeling. 1930. Ztschr. Geburtsh. Gynäk., 98: 103.
31. Barclay, A. E., J. Barcroft, D. H. Barron & K. J. Franklin. 1938. Brit. J. Radiol., 11: 570.

32. Haselhorst, G.   1929.   Ztschr. Geburtsh. Gynäk., 95: 400.
33. Scammon, R. E. & E. H. Norris.   1918.   Anat. Rec., 15: 165.
34. Schaeffer, J. P.   1914.   J. Exp. Med., 19: 129.
35. Mělka, J.   1926.   Anat. Anz., 61: 348.
36. Gross, R. E. & J. P. Hubbard.   1939.   J.A.M.A., 112 (1) : 729.

CHAPTER IV

THE BLOOD OF THE FETUS

SEVERAL opinions regarding development of the blood are reviewed in textbooks of embryology and histology[1, 2] and a more extensive consideration of this subject will be found in Downey's Handbook of Hematology.[3] The genesis of blood cells begins in all mammals shortly after the formation of germ layers. It starts in the wall of the yolk sac where mesenchymal cells retract their processes to assume more compact rounded forms freed from attachment to other cells. All types of blood cells arise from these hemoblasts. A similar transformation is encountered later in the body mesenchyme, liver, spleen and bone marrow as these structures develop. The first red blood corpuscles, derived from the primitive stem-cells of the yolk sac, play a transient functional rôle and are ultimately replaced by blood elements derived from other regions. Not until late embryonic stages do we normally find a division of blood forming tissues into myeloid for elaboration of red corpuscles and granulocytes, and lymphatic tissues for production of lymphocytes. Abnormally even after the adult stage has been reached lymphatic tissues and the loose connective tissue may lose their specificity and give rise to types of blood cells other than usually formed by them.

THE RED BLOOD CORPUSCLES

During the early part of prenatal life oxygen transport is effected by nucleated erythrocytes. As time goes on these are replaced by red blood corpuscles which have lost their nuclei, but some immature elements, the reticulocytes, are still observed in blood smears at birth. The total number of hemoglobin containing cells and corpuscles is small at first, for the blood is highly fluid, but increases as the end of gestation approaches. The diameter of the fetal red corpuscles is greater than in the adult, diminishing as development proceeds.[4-8]

These few facts have been known for many years and it is surprising that no one accepted their challenge to investigate this

interesting subject systematically until recently.[9-15]   All but the
most recent[16-18] contributions have been reviewed by Wintrobe
and Shumacker[19, 20] who described their own careful comparative
study in the pig, rat, rabbit, cat, dog and man.

At a period as early as it was possible to obtain adequate blood
samples from fetuses they found that the number of red blood
corpuscles, the amount of hemoglobin and the volume of packed
red corpuscles (hematocrit) are low in comparison with adult
blood of the same species.   The corpuscles are large, chiefly nucleated, and contain a correspondingly large amount of hemoglobin.

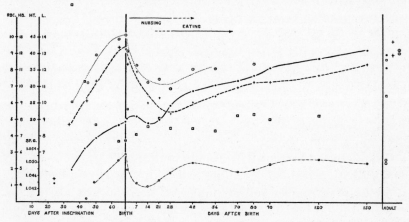

Fig. 19.—Number of red blood corpuscles (●) in millions, leukocytes (□) in
thousands, volume (hematocrit) of packed red corpuscles (⊙) in per cent, amount
of hemoglobin (+) in grams per 100 cc., and specific gravity (○) of the blood of
cats during prenatal and postnatal life until maturity.   Adult values for males are
higher than for females in all except specific gravity.   Each point represents an
average.

As development proceeds, the number of corpuscles, amount of
hemoglobin and volume of packed corpuscles increase, not in a
linear order, but more rapidly in early stages than later on near
term.   The mean corpuscular volume, mean corpuscular hemoglobin and proportion of immature forms of red blood corpuscles
decrease similarly.   But the mean corpuscular hemoglobin concentration remains about the same throughout the period studied.
The amount of hemoglobin available for transporting oxygen is a
function of the size and number of red blood corpuscles and its
concentration does not vary within individual corpuscles.   It was
observed that the period during which the greatest changes took

place seemed to correspond to the time during which hemopoiesis is most active in the fetal liver. The development of blood corpuscles and of hemoglobin in the cat, not only during prenatal life but onward to maturity, is illustrated in Fig. 19.[21]

In the species whose gestation periods are short, such as the rat,[18] the blood at birth is less like that of the adult than in species with long gestation periods, such as man. Even in the human fetus at birth, the number of red blood corpuscles in umbilical cord blood does not exceed that of the adult.[19, 20] This view may seem to be opposed to that which is generally taught, that the newborn has a higher red corpuscle count than the adult.[22] Actually it is not, for the infant has more red corpuscles per cubic millimeter of blood in circulation twenty minutes to half an hour after birth than it had in utero.[23] * Some investigators have reported more than seven million per cmm.[24, 25] and six million is not an excessive average figure for the first day of life. If there is any delay between birth and taking blood samples, a true picture of the condition in utero at the end of fetal life will not be obtained.

A sharp increase in red blood corpuscles is encountered in the cat on the day of birth.[21] This persists for a week, but the number declines to nearly the birth level by two weeks, rising again only after the kittens begin to feed themselves at three weeks (Fig. 19). Wintrobe and Shumacker suggested that high human red corpuscle counts after birth may be explained on the basis of dehydration, but we believe that the rôle played by dehydration on the first day of life of the cat is negligible. The specific gravity of the kitten's blood does not increase at birth, but on the contrary, decreases.[21] The transient rise in red corpuscle counts may be partly explained on the basis of splenic contractions, which have been demonstrated to start at birth in the sheep.[26]

The human fetus has about as many red blood corpuscles at the end of gestation as the adult but the corpuscles are of greater size; consequently the mean hemoglobin content and the total amount of hemoglobin in the blood are higher than in the adult. The amount of hemoglobin in the blood of the newborn has been reported by most investigators to be high; 20 gm. per 100 cc. of blood or even more is not uncommon.[27] The most recent estima-

* Statement based partly on a study now in progress.

tions made in blood drawn from the umbilical cord gave an average of 15.36 gm. per 100 cc.[28] This value correlates well with the oxygen capacity of human cord blood (see Chapter V). Hemoglobin decreases rapidly after birth. The high values for hemoglobin and the great number of corpuscles in the early postnatal period are undoubtedly related but there are other, poorly understood factors involved in this difference. In the kitten the curves for hemoglobin and corpuscles are not parallel until the fourth week of life. Perhaps this may be related to a substitution of new adult hemoglobin for the older fetal type.

An important conception of the development of blood has been proposed by Wintrobe and Shumacker. They observed that the developing fetal blood resembles that of patients with pernicious anemia who are being subjected to an effective, continuous and extremely potent stimulus to blood formation. They suggest that the anti-pernicious anemia factor of Castle may be the same or very similar to the substance which causes the blood of the fetus to develop. It is possible that the fetus obtains this from the mother. If too little is available to supply the needs of both mother and fetus a deficiency should manifest itself. Apparently it does so in "pernicious anemia of pregnancy" which can be controlled by administering liver extract and which even when untreated is relieved spontaneously by birth.[29, 30] If an inadequate amount of the anti-pernicious anemia factor is available to the fetus one might expect to observe effects upon the infant at birth. It has been shown that the incidence of primary anemia of the newborn is more common in multiple births, especially in premature multiple births, than in single births at full term.[31]

Wintrobe and his colleagues were unable to bring about changes in the blood of rabbit fetuses by feeding liver extract to the mothers or by injecting it into the placentas.[32] They concluded that the fetuses were taking up all the anti-pernicious anemia principle they could from normal maternal sources. Other investigators have treated pregnant rats with human and swine gastric juices, which contain the anti-pernicious anemia factor, and found that the diameter and mean volume of the fetal red blood corpuscles were reduced significantly at birth.[32-35] When the gastric juice had been inactivated by heating it produced no effect. On the other hand Wigodsky and Ivy, using large doses of potent anti-pernicious anemia factor, have been unable to confirm these results.[36]

Wintrobe and his colleagues made assays of fetal hog liver and placenta and found these organs lacking in physiologically demonstrable amounts of anti-pernicious anemia factor.[32] This suggested that a true physiological deficiency exists in the fetus and must be made up by drawing upon maternal sources. More recently however the livers of fetal calves have been demonstrated to contain large amounts of the active principle.[37]

OXYGEN CARRYING POWER OF FETAL BLOOD

Although oxygen transport will be considered in greater detail in the next chapter it should be pointed out now that a true difference between fetal and adult hemoglobin has been found in several species of animals. This was suspected for some time[38-41] and

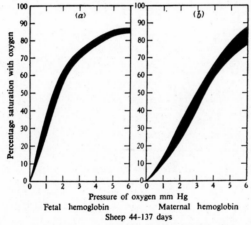

Fig. 20.—Oxygen dissociation curves for hemoglobin (a) of sheep fetuses, 44 to 137 days gestation, and (b) of their mothers. Limits fall within the shaded areas. Approximate temperature 19° C.; pH 9.3. (Hill; from Barcroft: Proc. Roy. Soc., Vol. 118, 1935, London.)

McCarthy has proved that fetal hemoglobin of the goat takes up oxygen more readily at low gas tensions than does maternal hemoglobin. This is illustrated in the oxygen dissociation curves of fetal and maternal hemoglobin reproduced in Fig. 20. The difference becomes less noticeable progressively until about five weeks after birth when the kid's hemoglobin attains adult characteristics.[42] Hall obtained similar results in fetal goats, rabbits and even

chicks.[43]   A very pronounced avidity for oxygen at low gas tensions
has been demonstrated in whole blood of calves near term.[44]
It was shown that differences in shape and position of fetal oxygen
dissociation curves of whole blood in relation to those of the
mother are inexplainable solely on the basis of greater alkalinity
of the mother's blood; they are governed by true chemical differences between the hemoglobins.

The human fetus at full term differs from all others which
have been studied, for it has been shown that its hemoglobin when
studied in dilute solution takes up oxygen less readily than does
that of the mother.[45, 46]   This will be seen in Fig. 21 which should
be contrasted with Fig. 20.   However, buffered (*p*H 7.4) suspen-

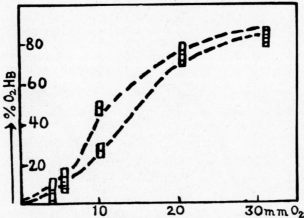

Fig. 21.—Oxygen dissociation curves for hemoglobin of the human fetus (right)
and mother (left).   (Haurowitz: Ztschr. Physiol. Chem., Vol. 232, 1935.)

sions of the fetal corpuscles, like whole fetal blood, become more
highly saturated with oxygen at low partial pressure than similar
suspensions of maternal corpuscles.[46]   The oxygen dissociation
curve of human fetal whole blood (see Fig. 27, p. 66) lies to the
left of that of the mother which in turn lies to the right of that for
normal human subjects.[47]

Species differences in avidity of the hemoglobin for oxygen
may be related to the degree of maturity reached at birth.   It
would be interesting to construct dissociation curves for human
fetal hemoglobin at the fifth or sixth month of gestation.   One can
not doubt that the fetus of every species possesses a mechanism for
assuring adequate intrauterine respiratory function throughout

prenatal life. Even though the number of red blood corpuscles may be less than that of the adult they are larger and contain more hemoglobin. In those species with great deficiency in number of corpuscles at birth there is a compensatory increase in the avidity with which their hemoglobins combine with oxygen.

THE LEUKOCYTES AND PLATELETS

At the time in early embryonic life when secondary erythrocytes are being formed by the yolk sac mesenchyme a few atypical megakaryocytes and leukocytes are similarly produced. Later, with intensive production of erythroblasts in the embryonic liver, granular leukocytes proliferate between the endothelium and the liver cells and a few megakaryocytes are formed there. The pseudopodia of the megakaryocytes produce the blood platelets. Neither granular leukocytes nor platelets are formed in great numbers until fetal hemopoietic activity shifts to the bone marrow about the third month. The lymphocytes of the body develop relatively later. They are formed by transformation of mesenchymal cells in the neighborhood of lymphatic vessels or in the walls of primitive lymph sacs.

Little is known about the number of leukocytes and platelets or of the numerical relations between granular and nongranular leukocytes. Kindred and Corey[13] attempted to determine the number of leukocytes in rat fetuses of different ages but found difficulty in differentiating them from immature forms of the red blood cells. It was apparent however that they increase about seven fold between the 16 and 35 mm. stages. It has been reported that both lymphocytes and polymorphonuclear cells are present in dog embryos at the time the limbs begin to grow out. But in fetuses 26 to 41 mm. long, at which time true neutrophilic leukocytes made their first appearance, the total white cell count was only 1,500 to 2,500 per cmm. of blood, with lymphocytes forming the greatest proportion.[25] Total nucleated cell counts at the middle of gestation in the cat seem to be about 16,000 per cmm.[21] The number decreases toward full term reaching 7,500 to 9,000 at birth. Thereafter it remains fairly constant at 8,000 to 9,000 until 120 days, as compared with 10,500 to 12,700 in the adult (Fig. 19). Bruner and his colleagues found less than one third as many leukocytes in the rat at birth as in the adult rat.[18]

At the time of birth of the human infant it has been reported that the blood contains great numbers of leukocytes; in fact one often hears the term, "leukocytosis of birth." Counts greater than 19,000 on the first day after birth, decreasing to about 9,000 by the tenth day, have been reported.[25] Japha found 36,000 leukocytes in the human newborn.[24] What factors, other than infections, may be responsible for the elaboration of such great numbers of leukocytes are unknown. Bayer has reported that inhalation of carbon dioxide led to increasing the number of granulocytes and breathing oxygen resulted in the formation of more lymphocytes.[48]

The number of blood platelets at birth has been reported to fluctuate widely. Results of a number of investigators have been summarized by Merritt and Davidson.[22] Nothing is known about them in prenatal life. The clotting time of the blood in early prenatal life appears to be long.

THE PLASMA

The blood has a high water content which declines as the time of birth approaches. It has been reported that water forms about 88 per cent of the human fetal blood at the third month of gestation and only 67 per cent at the ninth lunar month.[49] The umbilical vein blood has a water content of 79.5 per cent, as compared with 81.5 per cent in the mothers.[50] A sharp postnatal increase in water was observed, reaching a maximum of about 83 per cent 60 days after birth.

A few observations in the cat indicate that the specific gravity of the fetal blood is lower (about 1.04) at about the middle of fetal life than it is at full term (1.052). It is as high or slightly higher near the end of gestation than in the adult, diminishing gradually thereafter to reach its lowest level (1.043) about two weeks postnatally.[21]

The osmotic pressure of fetal blood colloids appears to be low in some species of animals, but data are incomplete. The subject will be discussed in Chapter VIII in relation to urine formation in the fetal kidneys.

THE CEREBROSPINAL FLUID

A recent study of the cerebrospinal fluid in dog fetuses has shed light upon the nature of its formation in the adult.[51] The blood plasma and the cerebrospinal fluid are alike in respect to their contents of chlorine, sodium and urea during the early part of fetal life. Between 40 and 43 days (fetuses 50 to 60 mm. long) the two fluids cease to be in balance. It is at this time that the cerebrospinal fluid is thought to change from an ultrafiltrate of the blood to a true secretion.

REFERENCES CITED

1. Arey, L. B. 1940. Developmental Anatomy. Saunders, Philadelphia.
2. Bloom, W. 1938. Maximow's Textbook of Histology, Saunders, Philadelphia.
3. Downey, H. 1938. Handbook of Hematology, Hoeber, N. Y.
4. Malassez, L. 1875. Arch. physiol. norm. path., Ser. 2, 2: 261.
5. Cohnstein, J. & N. Zuntz. 1884. Pflüger's Arch., 34: 173.
6. Malassez, L. 1889. Compt. Rend. Soc. Biol., 41: 2.
7. Jolly, J. 1906. Ibid., 60: 564.
8. Jolly, J. 1909. Ibid., 66: 136.
9. Nicholas, J. S. & E. B. Bosworth. 1928. Am. J. Physiol., 83: 499.
10. Knoll, W. 1929. Ztschr. mik.-anat. Forsch., 18: 199.
11. Zeidberg, L. D. 1929. Am. J. Physiol., 90: 172.
12. Deseö, D. 1929. Pflüger's Arch., 221: 326.
13. Kindred, J. E. & E. L. Corey. 1930. Anat. Rec., 47: 213.
14. Kindred, J. E. & E. L. Corey. 1931. Physiol. Zool., 4: 294.
15. Smith, C. 1932. J. Path. Bact., 35: 717.
16. Jones, J. M., M. E. Shipp & T. A. Gonder. 1936. Proc. Soc. Exp. Biol. & Med., 34: 873.
17. Barcroft, J. & J. A. Kennedy. 1939. J. Physiol., 95: 173.
18. Bruner, H. D., J. van de Erve & A. J. Carlson. 1938. Am. J. Physiol., 124: 620.
19. Wintrobe, M. M. & H. B. Shumacker. 1935. J. Clin. Inv., 14: 837.
20. Wintrobe, M. M. & H. B. Shumacker. 1936. Am. J. Anat., 58: 313.
21. Sweet, M. & W. F. Windle. 1940. Unpublished.
22. Merritt, K. K. & L. T. Davidson. 1933. Am. J. Dis. Child., 46: 990.
23. Schiff, E. 1892. Jahrb. Kinderhlk., 34: 159.
24. Japha, A. 1912. In Pfaundler & Schlossmann's Diseases of Children, 2: 131, Lippincott, Philadelphia.
25. Feldman, W. M. 1920. Ante-Natal and Post-Natal Child Physiology, Longmans, Green, London.
26. Taylor, D. B. & T. Gotsev. 1938. Cited by J. Barcroft, in The Brain and Its Environment, Yale Univ. Press, New Haven.
27. Lippman, H. S. 1924. Am. J. Dis. Child., 27: 473.
28. Waugh, T. R., F. T. Merchant & G. B. Maughan. 1939. Am. J. Med. Sci., 198: 646.
29. Bland, P. B., L. Goldstein & A. First. 1930. Ibid., 179: 48.
30. Beard, H. H. & V. C. Meyers. 1933. Am. J. Physiol., 106: 449.
31. Parsons, L. G. 1931. J.A.M.A., 97 (2) : 973.
32. Wintrobe, M. M., R. E. Kinsey, R. C. Blount & W. Trager. 1937. Am. J. Med. Sci., 193: 449.

33. Stasney, J. & G. M. Higgins. 1937. Staff Proc., Mayo Clin., 12: 490.
34. Stasney, J. & F. C. Mann. 1937. Ibid., 12: 699.
35. Schlicke, C. P. 1939. Ibid., 14: 145.
36. Wigodsky, H. S. & A. C. Ivy. 1938. Proc. Soc. Exp. Biol. & Med., 38: 787.
37. Wigodsky, H. S., O. Richter & A. C. Ivy. 1938. Am. J. Physiol., 123: 215.
38. Krüger, F. & W. Gerlach. 1927. Ztschr. f. ges. exper. Med., 54: 653.
39. Nicoletti, F. 1930. Arch. Antropol. Crim. Psichiat. Med. Legale, 50: 386.
40. Perrier, C. & P. Janelli. 1931. Arch. Fisiol., 29: 289.
41. Hentschel, H. 1928. Münch. med. Wchnschr., 75: 1237.
42. McCarthy, E. F. 1933. J. Physiol., 80: 206.
43. Hall, F. G. 1934. Ibid., 83: 222.
44. Roos, J. & C. Romijn. 1938. Ibid., 92: 249.
45. Haurowitz, F. 1935. Hoppe-Sey. Ztschr. physiol. Chem., 232: 125.
46. Hill, R. 1935. Cited by J. Barcroft. Proc. Roy. Soc. Lond., B, 118: 242.
47. Eastman, N. J., E. M. K. Geiling & A. M. DeLawder. 1933. Johns Hopkins Hosp. Bull., 53: 246.
48. Bayer, W. 1932. Jahrb. Kinderhlk., 134: 304.
49. Takakusu, S., K. Kuroda & K. Li. 1937. Keijo J. Med., 8: 58.
50. Kuroda, K. & K. Li. 1937. Ibid., 8: 40.
51. Flexner, L. B. 1938. Am. J. Physiol., 124: 131.

CHAPTER V

FETAL RESPIRATION

THE MECHANISM OF GASEOUS EXCHANGE

THE placenta is the organ for respiration in the fetus. Its maternal portions develop somewhat in advance of the parts contributed by the fetus with the result that the maternal vascular bed in the placenta reaches a large size while that of the fetus is al-

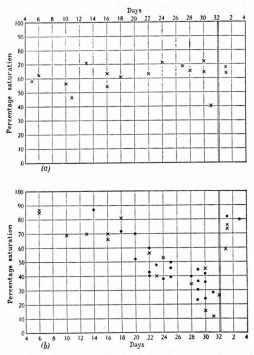

Fig. 22.—Percentage saturation of blood from the uterine veins during pregnancy in the rabbit. Non-pregnant uterine horn (*a*), pregnant horn (*b*). Birth indicated by the double line. Two series of experiments shown (● and ×). (Barcroft, et al.: Jour. Physiol., Vol. 83, 1934.)

most negligible. At the time the fetus is very small the maternal blood leaving the placenta is red because it has given up little oxygen to the fetus.[1, 2] As development of the fetus proceeds more and more oxygen is taken up in the placenta and the maternal veins leaving it become darker and darker, containing little oxygen indeed at the end of gestation.   This is illustrated in experiments designed to prevent pregnancy in one uterine horn of the rabbit.   The oxygen content of uterine vein blood remains constant throughout gestation on the non-pregnant side but declines progressively on the pregnant side (Fig. 22).

One can picture the placental circulation rather simply.   A well oxygenated stream of the mother's blood enters the placenta

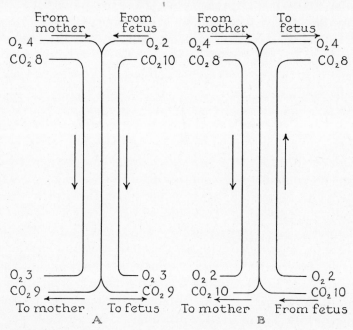

Fig. 23.—The exchange of oxygen and carbon dioxide in the placenta. If the maternal and fetal capillary streams course in the same directions (*A*), blood returning to the fetus will be as venous as that returning to the mother.   But if the streams course in opposite directions (*B*), it will come into equilibrium with that of the mother's arterial blood.   (Redrawn from Mossman: Am. J. Anat., Vol. 37, 1926.)

and comes into intimate contact with the fetal blood stream, poor in oxygen.   The two do not mix, but the degree of contact differs in various mammals.   One might think that the two streams should come into equilibrium in respect to the tensions of their blood gases, the fetal umbilical vein blood being as saturated or unsaturated as the uterine vein blood of the mother, and that the umbilical vein blood of the fetus should become progressively darker as gestation proceeds towards its termination. Actually this does not happen. The umbilical vein blood which courses toward the fetus is observed to be of much brighter color at term than that leaving the placenta on the maternal side. One explanation of this lies in an anatomical arrangement of the fetal and maternal vessels of the placenta. Mossman[3] has found that the fetal and maternal capillary streams, instead of coursing parallel to one another, actually flow in opposite directions in the rabbit placenta. A similar arrangement has been observed in the cat, dog, and other animals, but may not be present in all species. Thus the fetal blood has the opportunity to come into equilibrium, not with maternal venous blood, but with that at the arterial end of the maternal capillary bed. This mechanism is illustrated diagrammatically in Fig. 23.

The placenta reaches its maximum size while the fetus is still growing at a rapid rate. Nevertheless the volume of fetal blood traversing it increases in proportion to the weight of the fetus.[4] An increase in fetal blood pressure throughout pregnancy helps regulate the amount of blood passing through the placenta per minute. On the maternal side of the placenta, there is a somewhat smaller increase in the volume of flow, except at the end of gestation when it appears to be reduced (see Table 8, p. 32).

The fetus is provided with another mechanism to enable it to obtain oxygen readily in the placenta. Its hemoglobin differs from that of the mother's blood and the difference is such in most species that oxygen is taken up with greater ease at the low partial pressures which occur in the placenta. The total amount of oxygen taken up by the fetus increases progressively as the total number of corpuscles and their number per cubic centimeter of blood increase. The amount of oxygen utilized per gram of tissue remains nearly constant throughout the latter part of gestation in the sheep[5] at approximately 0.0043 cc. per minute.

THE OXYGEN CAPACITY OF THE BLOOD

A number of attempts have been made in recent years to shed light upon the question of fetal respiration by analyzing the blood on both sides of the placenta for oxygen and carbon dioxide. Since the original study of Cohnstein and Zuntz[6] several important investigations have been undertaken in the goat, sheep and human fetus and newborn.[7-17]   The hemoglobin of healthy adult systemic blood leaving the heart is approximately saturated (95 to 97 per cent) with oxygen.[18]   The blood contains on the average about 19 volumes of this gas per 100 cc. in the human female. The amount of oxygen carried in each cubic centimeter of the mother's blood in the latter part of gestation is somewhat less than this.   The amount of oxygen which the fetal blood can take up at any partial pressure does not depend entirely upon the capacity of the mother's blood for oxygen but upon other factors which will become evident when the nature of the maternal and fetal dissociation curves are considered.   Before discussing these relationships it will be of interest to compare the capacities of maternal and fetal bloods as found experimentally.   Results obtained at the end of gestation in human subjects are summarized in Table 11.[13, 15, 17]

TABLE 11

AVERAGE OXYGEN CAPACITY OF FETAL AND MATERNAL BLOOD IN MAN

	Fetal (vol. %)	Maternal (vol. %)
Adult (non-pregnant)	.....	19.00
At 8 months (1 Caesarean section)	18.14	17.26
At term (1 Caesarean section)	20.9	15.6
At normal birth (4 cases)	20.42	15.82
At normal birth (15 cases)	20.8	15.4
At normal birth (30 cases)	21.2 & 21.6*	.....
At normal birth (30 cases)	21.92	.....

* Umbilical artery and umbilical vein blood.

It will be seen that the capacity of the mother's blood to carry oxygen at the end of gestation is low in comparison with normal non-pregnant individuals.   This may be related to changes in the reaction of the blood (reduced alkalinity), decrease in number of maternal corpuscles in each cubic centimeter, and other factors. A marked decline in the oxygen content of cats' blood during the latter part of gestation has been observed.[19]

The capacity of the human fetal blood is higher than that of the mother and is about the same as that of the average normal adult male.   One might expect the fetal blood, which contains larger red corpuscles and considerably more hemoglobin than the adult, to be able to take up even greater quantities of oxygen.

However, it has been shown that human full-term fetal hemoglobin in dilute solutions takes up oxygen, gram for gram, less readily than does that of the adult.[20, 21]   The increased amount of hemoglobin little more than compensates for this deficiency.   This observation is in contrast with the determinations in other mammals.

Oxygen capacities have been determined in lower animals by a number of investigators, but most of the data are insufficient to demonstrate the relation to adults of the same species.   The studies in sheep and goats have shown that the mother's blood carries more oxygen per cubic centimeter than that of the fetus.[6-8]   Re-

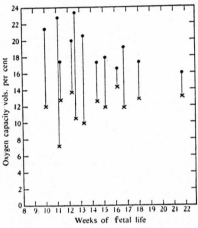

Fig. 24.—Comparison of oxygen capacities of maternal (●) and fetal (×) blood in the goat.   (Barcroft: Proc. Roy. Soc. London, Vol. 118, 1935.)

cent experiments in the ox and horse[11] suggest that the fetal blood at term has a slightly greater capacity than that of the mother and is therefore comparable with that of man.   The relationship between oxygen capacities in mothers and fetuses which Barcroft[9] found in the goat is illustrated in Fig. 24.   It will be seen that the fetal values increase as the maternal values decrease with the approach of birth.   This can be correlated with changing hemoglobin values.

Roos and Romijn followed the changes in oxygen capacity during the first few days after normal birth in cows and their calves.[11]   They found greater values for blood of the calves at birth than at 7½ to 8½ months gestation.   The oxygen capacity of the mother cows after delivery was greater, not only than those in late pregnancy, but also greater than the normal non-pregnant cows. The data are summarized in Table 12.

TABLE 12

AVERAGE OXYGEN CAPACITY OF BLOOD OF FETUS, OFFSPRING AND MOTHER IN THE OX

	Calves cc. O$_2$/100 cc. blood	Cows cc. O$_2$/100 cc. blood
11 non-pregnant cows.................	....	14.6
8 Caesarean sections at 7½ to 8½ months gestation......................	12.6	12.2
5 cows and 6 calves one hour or less after birth...........................	18.3	15.3

DISSOCIATION CURVES

The usefulness of a special fetal type of hemoglobin becomes apparent when the oxygen dissociation curves of fetal and maternal blood are compared. Conditions under which the fetal blood

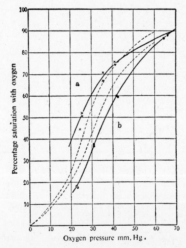

Fig. 25.—Oxygen dissociation curves of (a) fetal and (b) maternal blood of the goat at 18 to 19 weeks' gestation. Broken lines indicate limits of normal non-pregnant adult goat blood. (Barcroft, et al.: Jour. Physiol., Vol. 83, 1934.)

takes up oxygen are not nearly so advantageous as those occurring in the adult lungs. An oxygen tension of about 100 mm. Hg is found in the lungs but the tension, although not definitely determined, is considerably reduced in the placenta. Furthermore, the surface area of the human chorionic villi has been estimated to be only about half that of the lung alveoli at birth.[22]

Oxygen dissociation curves of maternal and fetal blood at the time of birth have been prepared by a number of investigators,[11, 12, 16, 23, 24, 25] but Barcroft and his colleagues[8] are the only ones who have compared the curves at different times during prenatal life. They studied the goat. It was found that the curve for

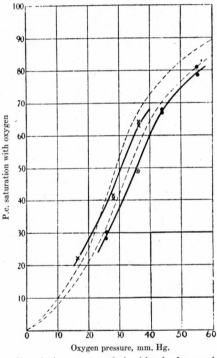

Fig. 26.—Oxygen dissociation curves of the blood of a newborn goat (left) and the mother (right). Broken lines indicate limits of normal non-pregnant adult goat blood. (Barcroft, et al.: Jour. Physiol., Vol. 83, 1934.)

maternal blood is displaced to the right of the normal adult curve from ten weeks on to birth, while that of the fetus gradually shifts to the left between the 10th and the 18th or 19th weeks and then returns at full term to approximately the position characterizing normal adult blood. The shape of the fetal curve differs in important respects from that of the mother. It is steeper at low oxygen pressures and crosses the maternal curve at about 70 mm. Hg. These results are illustrated in Figs. 25 and 26.

5

Oxygen dissociation curves for the human at full term are shown in Fig. 27. Here too the maternal curve lies to the right of that of the normal non-pregnant woman and the fetal curve is almost within the range of the non-pregnant woman, but lies to the left of the maternal curve and is of a different shape.[16] Some investigators[24] have found variations in human fetal oxygen dissociation curves at birth; the extremes are of two types, one of which is displaced farther to the left than the other and is less de-

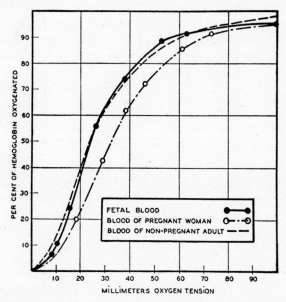

Fig. 27.—Oxygen dissociation curves of the blood of the human fetus at birth, its mother, and non-pregnant human adult. (Eastman, et al.: Johns Hopkins Hosp. Bull., Vol. 53, 1933.)

flected, crossing the maternal curve at higher oxygen tensions (85 mm. Hg) than the other (70 mm. Hg).

There is general agreement that the shift of the maternal oxygen dissociation curve to the right is due to a reduced alkalinity of the maternal blood. If this is the only factor governing the shift, the amount of displacement of the maternal curve must be definitely limited, for the reaction of the blood can not be greatly altered toward the acid side and still maintain normal health.

The shape of the fetal oxygen dissociation curve was found to be very different from that of the mother by most investigators.

Roos and Romijn[11] have obtained the most striking demonstration of this difference in the fetal calf. They found that the fetal blood can attain 50 per cent saturation with oxygen at an oxygen pressure of 11.5 mm. Hg, whereas that of the maternal blood becomes only about 8 per cent saturated at this tension. The maternal curve lies within the rather wide range of the normal non-pregnant cow, but the fetal curve is so far to the left that 90 per cent saturation with oxygen is reached when the mother's blood is less than 70 per cent saturated. Because the carbon dioxide dissociation curves of the fetus and mother almost coincide in the ox, the leftward displacement of the fetal oxygen dissociation curve cannot be explained on the basis of blood pH changes during pregnancy. It must be explained by a different type of hemoglobin in the fetus.

What is the significance of the observations outlined above? They show that there are species' differences, that the blood of some animals at birth is able to take up oxygen at approximately the same tension as that in the adult, but in others the fetal blood near term still takes it up with greater avidity than the adult and gives it up less readily. They demonstrate a mechanism which must be of inestimable value to successful intrauterine life. The spread between maternal and fetal oxygen dissociation curves indicates that oxygenation of the fetal blood is facilitated at the partial pressures which are physiologic in the placenta; the fetal blood can take up oxygen at a tension which causes the mother's blood to lose oxygen. It also makes the giving up of oxygen to the tissues of the fetus less easily effected; but this is not a serious obstacle to the fetus in utero which is relatively inactive and can get along with a slower tissue respiration. After birth it is desirable that these relationships be reversed. When the blood is oxygenated in the lungs it finds a greater oxygen tension prevailing there than in the placenta and the avidity of the fetal hemoglobin is no longer needed. On the other hand an active tissue metabolism calls for more efficient transfer of oxygen in the other direction at the peripheral capillaries. It would seem that there is an anticipation of this need some time before it becomes acute in the goat, for the fetal oxygen dissociation curve shifts gradually to the right and assumes a less inflected form during late gestation. The fetus is thus prepared in late fetal life for conditions it will meet after birth. In some newborn human infants the shift has not gone as far to the right as that of the newborn goat, and one may say that they correspond to goat fetuses about a month before birth.[26]

Carbon dioxide dissociation curves of fetal blood have been constructed in the goat, ox and man.[7, 11, 16, 24, 27, 28] The results of Eastman and his colleagues show that the fetal blood takes up carbon dioxide less readily and gives it up with greater ease than the non-pregnant adult blood at any given partial pressure of the gas.[16] However, the difference between mother and fetus in this respect is not marked. At about six weeks before term in the goat

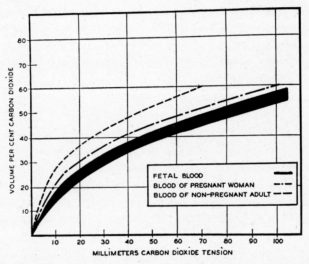

Fig. 28.—Carbon dioxide dissociation curves of the blood of the human fetus at birth, its mother and non-pregnant human adult. (Eastman, et al.: Johns Hopkins Hosp. Bull., Vol. 53, 1933.)

the fetal carbon dioxide dissociation curve lies on the left of the maternal curve.[27] By full term it has shifted well to the right.[7] The carbon dioxide dissociation curve of the pregnant cow was found to be displaced slightly to the right of that of the eight-month fetus.[11] The human carbon dioxide dissociation curves at birth are illustrated in Fig. 28.[16]

Calculations of the blood pH have been made from the carbon dioxide dissociation curves of goat's blood. Direct measurements in the blood of goats (glass electrode) coincide with the calculated pH values.[8] The fetal blood is less alkaline than that of the normal non-pregnant goat, falling within the range of pH 7.27–7.38, although it is more alkaline than that of the mother six weeks before the end of gestation. The lowered pH (decreased alkalinity) of the maternal blood is adequate to explain the shift to the right of the maternal oxygen dissociation curve. In normal human newborns the average pH of the umbilical artery blood has been found to be 7.32 and that of the umbilical vein blood, 7.35. The latter is about the pH of the mother's cubital vein blood, which is less alkaline than blood of normal non-pregnant individuals.[29]

A deficiency of carbonic anhydrase in fetal blood may explain the higher alkali reserve of the fetal blood plasma in goats six weeks before term.[30] The gradual shift to the right of the fetal dissociation curve for carbon dioxide during the latter part of gestation in the goat may indicate a gradual depletion of the alkali reserve.

OXYGEN AND CARBON DIOXIDE CONTENTS OF FETAL BLOOD

It is essential to learn how much oxygen the fetal blood actually contains as it leaves the placenta, at various places in the fetal circulation and when it returns again to the placenta. In the first place, how does the blood of the umbilical vein compare with that of the umbilical artery? A number of studies have been made in human fetuses at the moment of birth. Results fluctuate widely but this can be minimized to some extent by discarding cases of asphyxia at birth. One must bear in mind the technical difficulties encountered in obtaining fetal blood under physiologic conditions. There can be no doubt that maximum values for oxygen are more representative of the true condition than are averages which contain values obtained under partial anoxemia. Table 13 summarizes the more recent and reliable data from human infants obtained at the moment of birth.[12, 15, 25, 31] In addition Eastman[15] found 6.3 volumes per cent oxygen in the umbilical artery and 13.3 volumes per cent in the vein at one Caesarean section. Others who have drawn blood at Caesarean sections have obtained very low values for oxygen.

In half of Noguchi's experiments the infants had taken their first breath before blood samples could be drawn, but it was demonstrated that this did not significantly alter the analyses.

Haselhorst and Stromberger obtained similar results. Noguchi found no difference between 16 male and 14 female fetuses in the oxygen capacity of the blood.

TABLE 13

UPPER LIMITS AND AVERAGE VALUES FOR OXYGEN AND CARBON DIOXIDE IN BLOOD OF HUMAN INFANTS AT MOMENT OF BIRTH

Investigators	No. of cases	Umbilical artery				Umbilical vein			
		Vol. % O_2		Vol. % CO_2		Vol. % O_2		Vol. % CO_2	
		high	ave.	high	ave.	high	ave.	high	ave.
Haselhorst and Stromberger.....	22	.....	.....	.....	.....	14.88	10.14	47.88	40.71
	23	8.02	3.40	52.85	46.21	.....	.....	.....	.....
Bidone......	9	15.60	12.95	62.26	50.06	17.57	14.94	46.67	41.21
Eastman....	15	5.90	3.30	.....	.....	13.20	10.50	.....	.....
Noguchi.....	30	10.00	4.40	53.70	44.20	15.90	11.00	47.70	38.00

The percentage saturation of umbilical blood has been determined by the investigators cited above and the values are recorded in Table 14. We wish to stress the point that these are averages

TABLE 14

AVERAGE PERCENTAGE OXYGEN SATURATION OF HUMAN FETAL BLOOD AT BIRTH

	Umb. vein % sat.	Umb. artery % sat.
Haselhorst and Stromberger............	45.6	15.3
Eastman..............................	50.5	15.8
Eastman (Caesarean)	63.4	30.2
Noguchi.............................	57.7	21.7
Bidone (estimation)..................	73.6	63.8

and not upper limits. If we accept the figure 21 volumes per cent as the average oxygen capacity of human fetal blood at full term normal birth, and limit consideration to the highest values for oxygen content (Table 13), the umbilical vein blood appears to be between 63 and 84 per cent saturated at birth depending upon whose data are used. This assumption is not entirely valid because individual variation is to be expected in the amount of hemoglobin and oxygen capacity, but it may more nearly express the true condition of the fetal blood than do the mean figures in Table 14. Eastman found no more than 63 per cent saturation with oxygen in the umbilical vein,[15] but it is apparent that a much higher saturation was encountered by Bidone.[31]

The data available in lower animals are similar to those obtained in man. Great variation in the content of oxygen and carbon dioxide in the umbilical vessels has been reported in the goat, sheep, ox, dog and cat,[6, 7, 9, 11, 32-34] but if we admit only the highest values and consider that technical limitations may have reduced other values we are left with quite a different conception of respiratory conditions than we get from the average values. It would seem that the fetus does not thrive on venous blood.

The greatest number of analyses have been made by Barcroft and his colleagues who found that the superior limits of saturation with oxygen in the umbilical vein blood of fetal goats vary between 60 per cent and 87 per cent from the tenth to the nineteenth weeks of gestation, falling off to about 45 per cent in the last two weeks.[9] Similarly in the sheep, blood going to the fetus (umbilical vein) was found to be as much as 86 per cent saturated before the 137th day; after that lower values were the rule.[33] One of the most important observations on oxygen content of the blood of sheep fetuses 75 to 140 days gestation was made recently by Barcroft and Mason,[35] who devised a technique for obtaining blood from the umbilical vein or artery without delivering the fetus from the uterus and with a minimum of manipulation.* When this was done and the tendency toward placental separation avoided the blood going to the fetuses was found to be more than 90 per cent saturated with oxygen in half (five) their experiments and not less than 70 per cent saturated in the others. These results are shown in Table 15.

TABLE 15

PERCENTAGE OXYGEN SATURATION OF UMBILICAL AND UTERINE BLOOD IN THE SHEEP

	90% or over	89–80%	79–70%	69–60%	59–50%	49–40%
No. of cases: Umb. vein......	5	3	2	..	..	..
No. of cases: Umb. artery....	..	..	..	3	6	1
No. of cases: Uter. venule (Placental vein)...........	..	..	3	1	2	..

* In the final paper (Barcroft, J., J. A. Kennedy & M. F. Mason, 1940, J. Physiol., 97: 347) it was reported that the highest values were found between the 75th and 100th days of gestation and that they dropped considerably in the final week (a physiologic anoxemia).

It is evident that the oxygen content of the umbilical vein during life in utero is not as low as most studies lead one to believe. The better the technical procedures, the higher the values obtained. Other investigators have encountered 85 to 90 per cent saturation in the umbilical vein blood occasionally. Bidone[31] reported 17.6 volumes per cent oxygen (approximately 84 per cent saturated) in one human fetus before respiration started at birth. Roos and Romijn[11] found that the umbilical vein blood of the fetal calf of 7½ to 8½ months was saturated to a rather high degree, 90 per cent in one experiment.

Granting during fetal life that the blood coming from the placenta to the fetus by way of the umbilical vein is as much as 90 per cent saturated with oxygen does not entitle us to conclude that the fetal tissues are bathed continuously in blood so rich in this gas. The umbilical vein blood is diluted by reduced blood from the lower parts of the fetal body when it enters the fetal inferior vena cava. The degree of dilution is an unknown and perhaps not a constant factor. The inferior vena caval blood enters the right atrium of the heart and most of it passes into the left atrium by way of the foramen ovale, where it may be diluted a second time by blood returning from the fetal lungs (see Fig. 17, p. 43). This pulmonary blood is reduced because, even if little oxygen is removed by the tissues of the fetal lungs, much of the blood has already traversed the heart and upper parts of the body before passing to the lungs. The blood which is sent through the ascending aorta and the great vessels which spring from the aortic arch, *i.e.*, the blood which goes to the heart and brain, cannot be as saturated constantly with oxygen as that which enters the liver and inferior vena cava from the umbilical vein and ductus venosus.

Barcroft, Kramer and Millikan[10] have attempted to determine the degree of oxygen saturation in the carotid artery blood of sheep fetuses near the end of the gestation period. They used an ingenious mechanism consisting of a photoelectric cell and micro-lamp between which the carotid artery was placed. The blood acted as a red filter, oxyhemoglobin transmitting more light in the red end of the spectrum than reduced hemoglobin. Variations in the current from the photoelectric cell deflected a galvanometer mirror, and a beam of light from the mirror was used to record continuously on moving photographic paper. Respirations were recorded simultaneously. The mechanism was calibrated by analyses made with the Van Slyke manometric apparatus. Two records are reproduced in Figs. 29 and 30 and their interpretation in Fig. 31. It will be seen that complete saturation of the fetal blood was effected more readily when the lambs breathed oxygen than when they breathed air. In other experiments it was found that several hours were required for a complete saturation of the newborn blood without the aid of oxygen. The carotid artery

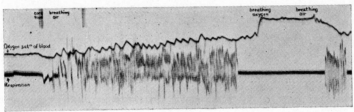

Fig. 29.

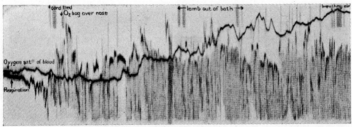

Fig. 30.

Figs. 29, 30.—Two photographic records of the changes in the oxygen saturation of the carotid blood during the initiation of respiration at birth in the sheep fetus. The sensitivity of the apparatus differed in the two experiments. For interpretation, see Fig. 31. (Barcroft, et al.: Jour. Physiol., Vol. 94, 1939.)

blood of sheep fetuses studied at Caesarean section was found initially to be between 32 and 70 per cent saturated with oxygen. How much higher than this the saturation is in the normal undisturbed fetus in utero we do not know.*

It has been very difficult to obtain satisfactory data on the blood gas contents of fetal blood because of technical difficulties. No one can doubt that operative procedures in exposing and open-

* It has been demonstrated recently that the carotid arterial blood is as much as 88 per cent saturated with oxygen in the sheep fetus prior to the last week of gestation (Barcroft, J., D. H. Barron, A. T. Cowie & P. H. Forsham, 1940, J. Physiol., 97: 338).

ing the uterus bring about changes in the respiratory relationships in the placenta. Any series of experiments will give some results below 25 per cent saturation with oxygen in umbilical vein blood, but one is justified in concluding that these values are not physiologic. The blood can actually be observed to darken before a sample can be drawn for analysis.

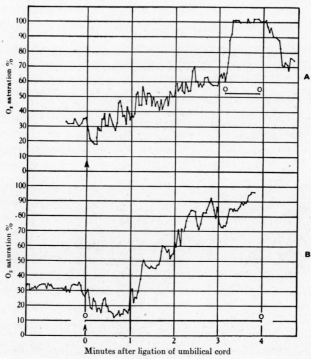

Fig. 31.—Interpretation (A) of Fig. 29 and (B) of Fig. 30, showing percentage saturation of the lamb's blood in the carotid artery at birth. Umbilical cord tied at ↑ ; lamb breathing oxygen at o—o. (Barcroft, et al.: Jour. Physiol., Vol. 94, 1939.)

At the end of fetal life there is some evidence that the oxygen carried by the umbilical vein blood is normally more reduced in goats and in cats than it was earlier.[9, 36] This constitutes a physiologic anoxemia. A factor which may play a part in regulating the amount of oxygen available to the fetus in the latter part of gestation in the cat, and which has been generally overlooked, is the motor activity of the uterus itself.[36]

Prelabor contractions of the uterus are of physiologic occurrence. It has usually been assumed that should they become severe they would block the fetal circulation through the placenta and lead to anoxemia in the fetus. Clark's[37] studies of blood pressure reflexes in cat fetuses pointed in this direction. In our laboratory we have observed that the contractions, providing they are not severe, are accompanied by improvement in color of the umbilical veins and that relaxation of the uterus results in darkening of the blood. Furthermore, analyses of the blood leaving the placenta on the maternal side, drawn from placental tributaries of the uterine vein, showed fluctuation in oxygen content, less oxygen being present during and just following a uterine contraction than in the interval of the relaxation. These values are the reciprocals of those observed on the fetal side of the placenta (umbilical vein). Blood was drawn from the placental tributaries without interfering at all with the fetuses and with little manipulation of the uterus. The pregnant animals were not anesthesized but had been decerebrated some time before. It is apparent that one can not speak of the conditions of fetal respiration, at least during the last few days of pregnancy, as though they were constant. They fluctuate normally from moment to moment; and whereas 95 per cent saturation with oxygen may be attained at times, it is doubtful if the average amount available to the fetus during the latter part of fetal life can be as great as it was earlier. The physiologic anoxemia of the fetus in late gestation will be given consideration in succeeding chapters. Other mechanisms have been suggested whereby dilation and contraction of uterine vessels play a part in regulating blood flow through the placenta.[38]

ASPHYXIA AT BIRTH

Much has been written concerning the conditions under which the fetus at birth fails to begin breathing. Asphyxia is the cause of death in an alarming number of cases, especially so as the demands for obstetrical anesthesia become more urgent. In recent years much light has been cast upon this subject by studies in the blood gases at birth. Some investigators have held to the old conception of asphyxia as an accumulation of carbon dioxide and have supposed that this was the case in the blood of newborns which failed to breathe.[39] In view of Henderson's[40] conception of asphyxia as a decrease in carbon dioxide as well as in oxygen one should expect that in the asphyxiated fetus, as well as in adults subjected to asphyxial conditions, the blood carbonates would shift to the tissues and hemoglobin, and the blood would contain less carbon dioxide.

Eastman[41, 42] appears to be the first investigator to demonstrate the truth of Henderson's theory in asphyxia neonatorum. He found that there is a reduction in oxygen content of umbilical vein blood to very low levels (sometimes less than one volume per cent), that the carbon dioxide is likewise lowered and that the pH of the blood may fall below 7.00 in fatal cases. Noguchi[17, 29] determined that there was some shift of plasma fluid in the fetus, probably to the fetal tissues but not across the placenta, that the oxygen was greatly lowered and that the carbon dioxide shifted to the cells from the plasma but was not greatly lowered in total amount. He also found a marked lowering of the pH of the blood and concluded that asphyxia neonatorum is a state of uncompensated alkali deficit in consequence of oxygen want. Cat fetuses depressed at experimental Caesarean section resemble human infants in asphyxia neonatorum. The oxygen content of their blood drops severely, and so does the carbon dioxide content.

REFERENCES CITED

1. Barcroft, J., W. Herkel & R. M. Hill. 1933. J. Physiol., 77: 194.
2. Barcroft, J., L. B. Flexner, W. Herkel, E. F. McCarthy & T. McClurkin. 1934. Ibid., 83: 215.
3. Mossman, H. W. 1926. Am. J. Anat., 37: 433.
4. Barcroft, J. & J. A. Kennedy. 1939. J. Physiol., 95: 173.
5. Barcroft, J., J. A. Kennedy & M. F. Mason. 1939. Ibid., 95: 269.
6. Cohnstein, J. & N. Zuntz. 1884. Pflüger's Arch., 34: 173.
7. Huggett, A. St. G. 1927. J. Physiol., 62: 373.
8. Barcroft, J., R. H. E. Elliott, L. B. Flexner, F. G. Hall, W. Herkel, E. F. McCarthy, T. McClurkin & M. Talaat. 1934. Ibid., 83: 192.
9. Barcroft, J. 1935. Proc. Roy. Soc., Lond. B, 118: 242.
10. Barcroft, J., K. Kramer & G. A. Millikan. 1939. J. Physiol., 94: 571.
11. Roos, J. & C. Romijn. 1938. Ibid., 92: 249.
12. Haselhorst, G. & K. Stromberger. 1930. Ztschr. Geburtsh. Gynäk., 98: 49.
13. Haselhorst, G. & K. Stromberger. 1931. Ibid., 100: 48; 1932. Ibid., 102: 16.
14. Haselhorst, G. 1931. Arch. Gynäk., 144: 558.
15. Eastman, N. J. 1930. Johns Hopkins Hosp. Bull., 47: 221.
16. Eastman, N. J., E. M. K. Geiling & A. M. DeLawder. 1933. Ibid., 53: 246.

17. Noguchi, M. 1937. Jap. J. Obst. Gyn., 20: 218.
18. Barcroft, J. 1925. The Respiratory Function of the Blood, Cambridge Univ. Press.
19. Steele, A. G. & W. F. Windle. 1938. J. Physiol., 94: 525.
20. Haurowitz, F. 1935. Hoppe-Sey. Ztschr. physiol. Chem., 232: 125.
21. Hill, R. 1935. Cited by J. Barcroft, Proc. Roy. Soc., Lond. B, 118: 242.
22. Christoffersen, A. K. 1934. Compt. rend. Soc. Biol., 117: 641.
23. Anselmino, K. J. & F. Hoffmann. 1930. Arch. Gynäk., 143, 477.
24. Leibson, R. G., I. I. Likhnitzky & M. G. Sax. 1936. J. Physiol., 87: 97.
25. Noguchi, M. 1937. Jap. J. Obst. Gyn., 20: 358.
26. Barcroft, J. 1938. The Brain and Its Environment, Yale Univ. Press, New Haven.
27. McCarthy, E. F. 1933. J. Physiol., 80: 206.
28. Keys, A. B. 1934. Ibid., 80: 491.
29. Noguchi, M. 1937. Jap. J. Obst. Gyn., 20: 248.
30. Roughton, F. J. W. 1935. Physiol. Rev., 15: 241.
31. Bidone, M. 1931. Ann. ostet. ginec., 53: 197.
32. Kellogg, H. B. 1930. Am. J. Physiol., 91: 637.
33. Barcroft, J. 1936. Physiol. Rev., 16: 103.
34. Steele, A. G. & W. F. Windle. 1939. J. Physiol., 94: 531.
35. Barcroft, J. & M. F. Mason. 1938. Ibid., 93: 22P.
36. Windle, W. F. & A. G. Steele. 1938. Proc. Soc. Exp. Biol. & Med., 39: 246.
37. Clark, G. A. 1934. J. Physiol., 83: 229.
38. Schmitt, W. 1925. Deut. med. Wchnschr., 51 (1) : 189.
39. Kane, H. F. & J. Kreiselman. 1930. Am. J. Obst. Gyn., 20: 826.
40. Henderson, Y. 1928. J.A.M.A., 90: 583.
41. Eastman, N. J. 1932. Johns Hopkins Hosp. Bull., 50: 39.
42. Eastman, N. J. & C. M. McLane. 1931. Ibid., 48: 261.

CHAPTER VI

FETAL RESPIRATORY MOVEMENTS

IT is commonly taught that the fetus in utero is apneic. However, this concept has been challenged from time to time and some investigators have declared that respiratory movements occur regularly throughout prenatal life under normal physiologic conditions. No one doubts that mammalian fetuses are capable of performing rhythmical movements which take the form of shallow rapid breathing or even of dyspneic gasping. Movements of this nature are frequently encountered upon opening the uterus of a pregnant laboratory animal. The literature contains many articles in which mention of such activities has been made. The early studies were reviewed by Preyer.[1] Human fetuses, aborted or removed surgically from the uterus, show the movements in question as early as the twelfth week of gestation.[2] One of the most striking examples of respiration in immature forms is encountered in the opossum.[3] Although this animal is born after a sojourn of only 12-13 days in utero (or in the tubes, as a blastocyst) it is able to breathe and to make its way unassisted to the pouch where it reassumes dependence upon the mother. Most studies in other animals have employed fetuses removed from the uterus and one may well question whether any of them were representative of the normal. It is not permissible to conclude, on the basis of observations made under conditions which prejudice the placental exchange mechanism, that respiratory motor phenomena are indulged in normally by the fetus throughout prenatal life.

RESPIRATORY MOVEMENTS IN THE INTACT ANIMAL

Let us examine the evidence of fetal movements resembling respiration in the intact animal. In 1888 Ahlfeld, a German gynecologist, described certain rhythmical fetal movements which he and a pupil observed in patients during the latter weeks of pregnancy.[4, 5] Superimposed upon the slow excursions of the gravid abdomen which resulted from maternal respirations they could see more rapid rhythms which appeared to be due to activities of the fetus.   Ahlfeld proposed that the fetus was making respiratory efforts and thought it must aspirate its amniotic fluid into the major respiratory passages.   Many protested this theory, but as recently as 1905 he reiterated his views and published convincing graphic records of these movements.[6]   The intrauterine respiratory movements have been observed by other investiga-

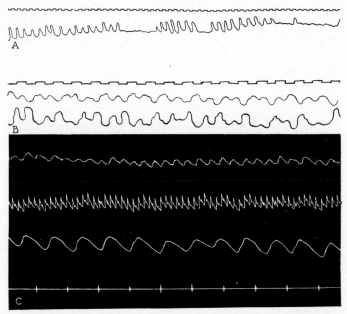

Fig. 32.—Human intrauterine respiratory movements.   *A*, Interrupted rhythms at a frequency of about 52 per minute.   *B*, Movements recorded from fetal abdomen and chest simultaneously; about 80 per minute.   (Ahlfeld: Monatschr. Geburtsh. Gynäk., Vol. 21, 1905.)   *C*, Intrauterine fetal respiratory movements (upper), maternal carotid pulse, maternal respirations and time in 4 second intervals (lower) before labor began.   (K. Reifferscheid: Pflüger's Arch., Vol. 140, 1911.)

tors,[7] but the theory of aspiration of fluid has not been generally accepted and it is usually concluded that the fetal glottis remains closed.   The question has been raised again recently by investigators[8] who are of the opinion that the human fetus executes rhythmical respiratory movements normally and that these serve to draw amniotic fluid into the lungs.   It was even suggested that this fluid may assist in the development of the lung alveoli.   Tracings illustrating the character of human fetal respiratory movements are reproduced in Fig. 32. A striking comparison of intrauterine fetal and early postnatal respiratory records will be seen in Fig. 33.

The principal objection to the current view is that the movements in question are not always, in fact not often, manifested by the human fetus. One must watch patiently to see them and when they do appear they are usually transient. If they were commonly encountered in the human, one should expect to see them in

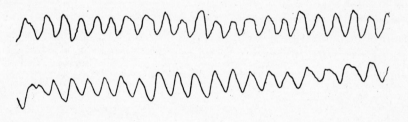

Fig. 33.—Comparison of human intrauterine respiratory movements (upper) with those of a five day old infant. Time, 4 second intervals. (K. Reifferscheid: Pflüger's Arch., Vol. 140, 1911.)

some other animals too. Fetal respiratory-like activities are rarely apparent in cats and guinea pigs but have been seen a day or so before birth.[9] The question of aspiration by the fetus will be considered later. It is pertinent first to investigate the factors which govern the manifestation of fetal respiratory-like movements.

RESPIRATORY MOVEMENTS UNDER EXPERIMENTAL CONDITIONS

Respiratory movements have been studied recently in a number of laboratory animals including the rat, guinea pig, rabbit, sheep and cat.[9-18] They have been observed in human beings under somewhat similar conditions.[19-23] There is little doubt that their occurrence and characteristics are influenced by the experimental conditions. These must be evaluated critically.

In the first place, anesthesia seems to alter the threshold of the fetal respiratory center and for this reason most investigators have tried to avoid using it. Ether administered to the mother anesthetizes the fetuses which then rarely exhibit respiratory activities until after placental circulation has been interrupted; at that time they take the form of dyspneic gasping. Urethane likewise depresses the rapid rhythms of the shallow respiratory movements.[24] Doses of nembutal which anesthetize the mother similarly depress the fetus.[25] Although sodium amytal is said to have no effect upon the fetus of the rat when given to the mother[26] and not to pass the placental barrier readily, further consideration should be given to this question. It is possible that some asphyxial types of anesthesia first stimulate respiratory movements in normally apneic fetuses,[9] but there is little doubt that their continued use results in depression. Cyclopropane (30 per cent) is said to be about the only inhalation anesthetic which does not seriously

Fig. 34.—Two portions of a continuous crystograph record of uterine motility, maternal respiration and intrauterine fetal respiratory movements on the 67th day of gestation in the cat (end of gestation). The animal had been decerebrated by the anemia method; no anesthesia was used during the experiment; the abdomen was not opened. The major fluctuations at the beginning of each tracing indicate relaxation of the uterus after a contraction occurring one minute before the arrow (↑). The large secondary waves are the maternal respirations (17 per minute). The smallest waves are intrauterine fetal respiratory-like movements occurring at approximately 120 per minute, slower at first than when they are well under way. Five minutes between relaxations 1 and 2.

affect the respiratory activities of fetuses and still gives surgical anesthesia.[27]

Various experimental procedures have been employed to avoid the use of general anesthetics. Spinal anesthesia can be used successfully in the larger species. Spinal cord section if performed long enough beforehand to allow recovery from shock may be satisfactory in those animals which are rather docile anyway. Decerebration is to be recommended in other forms. After preparing an animal near term by one of these methods it is occasionally possible, without opening the maternal abdomen, to see movements of a rhythmical nature resembling fetal "breathing." In Fig. 34 such fetal respiratory movements are shown (after decerebration of the cat) superimposed upon maternal respirations. This curve was obtained by means of a crystograph activated by amplified potentials from an oscillating circuit, any movements

6

on the surface of the cat's abdomen changing the frequencies of oscillation. To what extent decerebration, spinal cord section or other preparatory surgical procedures were responsible for instituting the respiratory movements, is not known.

When the pregnant animal is placed in a bath of warm saline solution, the abdomen opened and the uterus exposed, it is possible to observe fetal activities more directly. Rabbit and guinea pig fetuses near term can be seen quite easily through the thin uterine wall. Body form of other species is readily distinguishable. During the course of 30 minutes or more of observation, respiratory rhythms of fetal movements usually make their appearance in the cat. The longer the uterus has been exposed and the nearer the end of gestation, the more frequently these activities manifest themselves. They rarely continue for more than a few seconds but start and stop at fairly regular intervals. This intermittent occurrence of brief rhythms is associated with motility of the uterus in the cat. Mild contraction of uterine muscle is accompanied by a period of fetal quiescence; relaxation of the muscle leads to a rhythm of respiratory movements. Fetal activities of a respiratory nature are rarely if ever seen in the unopened uterus before the last two weeks of gestation in the cat. This is not because it is more difficult to visualize younger fetuses, for as we shall soon see it is possible to induce the movements in question by appropriate experimental methods as early as the middle of prenatal life.

Most of the earlier studies on respiratory movements of fetuses were made after delivering the specimens from the uterus under warm saline solutions, leaving the placenta attached to the uterine wall. It has often been erroneously assumed that circulation and gaseous exchange can thus be maintained adequately and that observations made in the fetus under such conditions are representative of activities occurring normally in the intact animal.

When a cat fetus has been determined to be apneic in utero and is then carefully but quickly delivered through a small incision in the least vascular portion of the uterus at one end of the zonary placenta it commonly begins to execute respiratory movements within a very short period of time; often this is a matter of one minute or less. The blood of the umbilical veins darkens perceptibly at delivery and the manifestation of respiratory movements is associated with such darkening in cat fetuses during the third quarter of gestation.[18]

Fetal respiratory movements have been studied in other mammals under similar conditions.[13, 14] It was found that the earliest respiratory movements of sheep fetuses can be elicited by mechanical stimulation at about 38–39 days of gestation. The first rhythms of movement seem to be enhanced by putting pressure upon the amnion and thus indirectly stimulating the fetus. Later they seem to occur spontaneously, but it is never possible to avoid some mechanical disturbance of the fetus and the manipulation of the uterus itself may have been a factor in producing the "spontaneous" activities. Urethane or spinal anesthetics were employed for the ewes.

Rhythmical respiratory movements have been studied in rabbits after sectioning the spinal cords of the pregnant does.[12] The activities were manifested both before and after delivering the fetuses from the exposed uterus. Most of the rabbits were at term or had passed the time birth should have occurred normally, labor having been inhibited by hormone treatment. It is possible that the post-mature fetuses suffered inefficient placental exchange of oxygen and carbon dioxide; it has been shown that all rabbit fetuses die by the 36th day (normally delivery occurs at 31 or 32 days) when labor is inhibited.[28]

From the various experimental studies it is clear that mammalian fetuses are capable of exercising their respiratory muscles and of doing so rhythmically after the fashion of air-breathing animals rather early in prenatal life. But mammalian fetuses do not execute rhythmical respiratory movements continually in utero unless certain unfavorable conditions are set up. Even near the termination of life in utero when the efficiency of the placenta in relation to the greatly enlarged fetus has declined and when one might expect to find a physiologic anoxemia, it is surprising how seldom the activities in question can be observed in the intact animal.

RELATION OF OXYGEN AND CARBON DIOXIDE TO RESPIRATORY MOVEMENTS

Since the blood of the fetus comes almost into equilibrium with that of its mother in respect to tensions of carbon dioxide and oxygen in the placental capillary bed one may well raise the question: why does the fetal respiratory center not respond as readily as that of its mother? It has been assumed that the threshold is higher than that of the mother.[29, 30] If this is one of the main factors in preventing continuous fetal respiratory movements from manifesting themselves normally in utero it should be possible to find a carbon dioxide level at which the fetal center will respond; or perhaps the threshold of the fetal center can be lowered experimentally until fetal respiratory movements begin.

It has been suggested that accumulation of metabolic carbon dioxide may be the agent starting these movements in cat and rat fetuses.[10, 16] Barcroft and his colleagues[31] administered atmospheres rich in carbon dioxide to pregnant sheep without inducing respiratory movements in the fetuses. However, the animals had been anesthetized with urethane and it is possible that the threshold of the center had been raised by this drug to a level which could not be reached by the maximum concentration the blood could carry. The effect of giving carbon dioxide to pregnant rabbits has been investigated.[12] The fetuses were already executing respiratory movements and the rate of the fetal rhythm was not greatly altered by the gas. The only positive results were obtained in cat fetuses,[18] mostly in the third quarter of the gestation period; the fetuses were apneic at the time of experimentation. Some were delivered from the uterus with placental circulation intact and others were observed through the unopened uterus. When the mother cats breathed atmospheres of oxygen containing 8 to 10 per cent carbon dioxide, rhythms of rapid respiratory movements appeared both in the delivered and the intact fetuses concomitantly with the increase in rate and amplitude of maternal breathing. Substitution of 15 to 20 per cent carbon dioxide in oxygen led to depression of the fetal respiratory efforts, which became very deep gasps at a slow rate. The cat was then allowed to breathe air again and a "rebound hyperpnea" often followed in the fetuses, presumably as the carbon dioxide level readjusted itself in the fetal blood. One of these experiments is illustrated in Fig. 35.

Administration of mixtures of 5 to 8 per cent oxygen in nitrogen to the mother cats brought about cyanosis, indicated by darkening of the uterine vessels, and respiratory movements of the previously apneic fetuses began promptly. Compression of the umbilical cord produced similar results in exaggerated form and more quickly. In large fetuses of sheep it was found that compression of the umbilical arteries alone led to respiratory activity but that this activity was delayed and did not manifest itself so soon as it did after compressing the veins too.[31] This indicates that the fetus was able to draw upon blood in the placenta and obtain a little more oxygen while the veins were intact. Many other investigators have reported that interruption of the placental circulation brings about respiratory efforts in the fetus.[1, 10,]

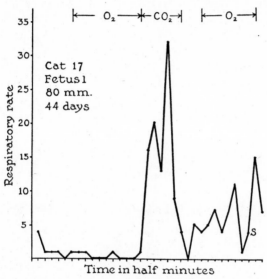

Fig. 35.—Effect of an 8 to 10 per cent carbon dioxide-oxygen mixture, breathed by the mother, in initiating rhythmical respiratory movements in a cat fetus delivered at Caesarean section but with placental circulation intact. Respiratory rate in half minutes. (Windle, et al.: Physiol. Zool., Vol. 11, 1938.)

[16, 32, 33, 34] Usually these were of the dyspneic gasping type. When asphyxia is avoided fetal respiratory movements of the cat occur at rates as high as 120 per minute, commonly more than 60 per minute.

Atmospheres deficient in oxygen breathed by full term guinea pigs on which no surgery had been performed and no anesthetic used caused rhythmical respiratory movements to start in the previously apneic fetuses.[9] Usually the first activities to appear were rather fast rhythms of movement which resembled shallow respirations. With more marked cyanosis these became stronger

and slower.   Ultimately only slow rhythmical gasps were seen in
the fetuses.   Upon relieving the asphyxia the rapid rhythms returned and then they too stopped, the fetuses becoming apneic
again with return of normal oxygenation.

Blood-gas analyses have been made from samples withdrawn
anaerobically from the umbilical veins of cat fetuses delivered
from the uterus but in which the placental circulation was still
intact.[35]   It was found that the oxygen content was low, the blood
being little more than 50 per cent saturated in those fetuses which
were executing rhythmical respiratory movements at the time of
sampling.   When oxygen saturation dropped to about 25 per cent
or less the fetuses gasped or became depressed to the point of complete inactivity.   Under the conditions of the experiments it was
less possible to relate the presence or absence of the movements
in question to carbon dioxide than to oxygen content.   However,
in the presence of the higher oxygen levels (40-50 per cent saturation) the carbon dioxide content was greater than it was when
the oxygen level was markedly lowered; in the former instances
the fetuses executed rapid rhythms, whereas in the latter they
became inactive and depressed.   Arrhythmical deep gasps appeared
when the carbon dioxide was high and the oxygen low.

It was not possible to obtain blood from the cat fetuses without incising the uterus and disturbing relationships there to some
extent; consequently one does not know what the oxygen level is
in utero.   However, it was evident that respiratory efforts often
began as the fetus was being delivered and as the umbilical vein
blood was darkening.   Probably a higher oxygen level is maintained in the normal undisturbed uterus than the highest value
obtained at experimentation would indicate.   This is true in
other species.   The sheep in late fetal life is apneic in utero; correlatively its umbilical vein blood, obtained without removing the
lamb from the uterus, is highly saturated, exceeding 90 per cent
in some.[36]   But when the lamb is delivered into a bath of saline
solution with its placental circulation intact the blood becomes
reduced.[37]

In the human at normal birth, apnea prevails when the blood
is about 50 per cent saturated with oxygen irrespective of the
carbon dioxide content,[38] but respiration starts readily.   Some
higher values have been obtained in apneic human fetuses[39, 40] as

well as in the calf.[41]   One may infer from these experiments that
the normal apnea of fetuses in utero is associated with a degree of
oxygenation exceeding about 40 or 50 per cent saturation, that as
this becomes reduced rhythms of active respiratory movements appear, but that depression of the oxygen level much below 25 per
cent saturation leads to gasping and ultimately to complete inactivity comparable with that in asphyxia neonatorum.*

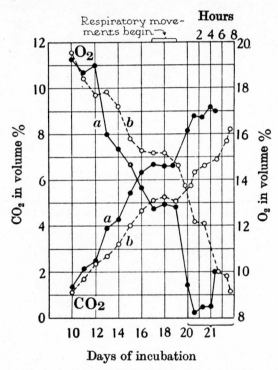

Fig. 36.—Oxygen and carbon dioxide contents of the atmosphere of the air space
in two hen's eggs taken at daily intervals during incubation. Respiratory movements begin at the plateau between 17 and 19 days. (Romijn and Roos: Jour.
Physiol., vol. 94, 1938.)

Experiments in mammalian fetuses have been confirmed in the
incubating eggs of chicks and ducks.[42-45]   It was possible to con-

* Barcroft and his colleagues have demonstrated recently that apnea prevails
in the sheep fetus when the blood going to the fetal brain is about 60 to 80 per
cent saturated with oxygen and when that leaving it is 30 per cent or more saturated. Lower values were encountered during the last prenatal week. Respiratory
movements occurred when the blood leaving the brain was 10 to 25 pr cent saturated (Barcroft, J., D. H. Barron, A. T. Cowie & P. H. Forsham 1940, J. Physiol.,
97: 338) .

trol physiologic conditions more precisely in the bird than in the mammal. Although space limitations do not allow discussion of these studies here it should be pointed out that our knowledge of the atmospheres breathed by the bird throughout incubation is reasonably complete. A nice correlation can be drawn between the decline in oxygen concentration, the elevation of carbon dioxide and the appearance of respiratory movements.[46] This is illustrated in Fig. 36.

We learn from the various experiments with carbon dioxide excess and oxygen want in mammals and in birds that the fetal respiratory center responds much as does that of the adult, but there is one very marked difference between fetus and adult. Greater concentrations of carbon dioxide and more severe degrees of oxygen deficiency must come into play in the former before results are obtainable. In other words the fetal respiratory center seems to have a high threshold.

OTHER FACTORS IN THE DEVELOPMENT OF RESPIRATION

Not all mammals are capable of performing rhythmical respiratory movements at the same period in prenatal life. One finds some species more precocious than others. As has already been indicated, the newborn opossum "embryo" breathes about 13 days after conception. In the more advanced fetus of the sheep respiratory movements have been observed at the end of the first quarter, but still at a relatively earlier time than in the cat. The latter reaches nearly the middle of gestation before rhythmical respiratory movements can be induced. The human fetus has accomplished necessary growth by the end of the twelfth week of intrauterine existence.

Muscles and peripheral nerves are laid down long before fetal respiratory movements begin. It is quite clear that the accomplishment of rhythmical movements awaits further development of a central nervous mechanism. In the 15 mm. cat embryo intrinsic growth of spinal neurons and their connections have reached the point at which the first simple reflexes are possible.[47] From this time onward the process of nervous integration proceeds, new responses accompanying new nervous connections and simple activities becoming more complex.[48] Most of the responses of which a cat embryo of 20 mm. length, delivered with placental circulation intact, is capable appear to be almost purposeless. The rhythmical respiratory movements which make their appearance just before the 30 mm. stage are among the first to foretell a usefulness. However, the behavior pattern that makes possible rhythmical respiration is not a new thing; it is the rhythmicity that is new. Even before 30 mm., in fact as early as 20 mm., integrated but arrhythmical contractions of the future respiratory muscles occur when adequate stimuli are used to elicit them. Their resemblance to gasps is often striking. It seems probable in all the species which have been studied (rat, rabbit, guinea pig, cat, sheep, goat and man) that the motor pattern responsible for respiration is a very fundamental one. It consists of the appropriate muscles with their motor neurons. Respiratory acts manifest themselves under experimental conditions as soon as the central nervous mechanism for simultaneously discharging these groups of efferent neurons is developed. The period in fetal life at which this occurs is that during which there is an extensive development of connecting neurons of the reticular formation in the medulla oblongata and downward growth into the spinal cord of many longitudinal nerve fibers. Ground bundles, reticulospinal and similar phylogenetically old pathways have been laid down. The appearance of rhythmicity has not been correlated with any specific change in the central nervous system. Growth there has gone so far at 30 mm. that many of the structures characterizing the adult tegmentum have appeared. Multiplication of association neurons, and consequently of possible connections in neuron circuits, seems to characterize this stage in fetal brain growth.

A very ingenious theory concerned with neural control of respiratory movements in the sheep fetus has been proposed.[14] In the first place, it was assumed that the rapid rhythmical movements seen in 40-day-old sheep fetuses delivered at experimental Caesarean section are physiologically normal and that they result from some poorly understood rhythmical (autochthonous?) discharge of the respiratory center. The progressive change in character of these movements which is encountered during further development of the fetus and which culminates in complete apnea at about 60 days gestation, it was suggested, is due to the progressive downgrowth of new inhibitory neurons from the higher nervous centers. Asphyxia or experimental transection of the brain-stem between midbrain and pons appeared to abolish the inhibitory influences and leave a more primtive respiratory pattern like that seen in fetuses 50 days old or less. Although it is certain that all fetal activities change with the gradual maturation of nerve tracts in the brain, the experimental data do not prove the theory proposed and alternative theories may be equally well supported. It is quite possible that expiratory and pneumotaxic centers are dominant to the inspiratory center in fetal life. Inhibition of the inspiratory center by impulses from the pneumotaxic center or continual stimulation of the expiratory center would account for the unexpanded chest and collapsed lungs.[49] Perhaps in the early sheep fetus the inspiratory center has not yet come under the dominance of higher neurons.

The importance of muscle tonus in establishing conditions favorable to lung ventilation at birth has been stressed by some.[50] If the fetus in utero possessed the tonus of a healthy newborn it is difficult to see how it could fit itself to the space allowed and how it could keep from filling its lungs with fluid. In one experiment[31] action potentials from electrodes which were placed in the fetal muscles were demonstrated each time the specimen was lifted out of its warm saline bath. These stopped when it was returned to the bath (see Fig. 63, p. 176). It seems probable that the increase in stimulation of afferent neurons attendant upon delivering the fetus from a warm aqueous habitat to the outside air plays an important part in increasing the tonus of the muscles in consequence of setting up activity in neuron circuits. This neural activity may serve to lower the respiratory center's threshold and allow a lower level of carbon dioxide to stimulate it to action.

Others have found that the respiratory center of the fetal goat four to six weeks from full term responds to afferent nerve stimulation like that of the adult, but it requires much stronger stimulation.[30] It was inferred that the fetal center has a higher threshold. By decerebration of the fetus it was demonstrated that the higher threshold was not due to inhibitory influences from the cerebrum.

That the apnea of intrauterine life may be due to a physiologic anemia of developmental origin has been suggested.[51] Occlusion of the umbilical arteries at birth is said to increase peripheral resistance in the aorta, raise the systemic pressure and induce a marked cerebral flow. This relieves the anemia, the high carbon dioxide concentration prevailing acts as a respiratory stimulus and respiration is initiated.

ASPIRATION OF AMNIOTIC CONTENTS

In the early paragraphs of this chapter mention was made of the suggestion that the fetus normally aspirates amniotic fluid. Granting that respiratory movements can and do occur occasionally in utero toward the end of gestation, what is the evidence that they cause aspiration of amniotic contents? It has been pointed out that dyes injected into the amniotic sac can be found in fetal lungs after removing the fetuses.[8, 52-54] But in none of these experiments was anoxemia rigidly ruled out of consideration. Indeed, in some it is quite obvious that it may have been a factor in starting the respiratory activity. It is known that vernix caseosa is sometimes found in the lungs of infants which have survived birth a short time. In a large series of autopsies with microscopic study Farber and Sweet[55] found that only 15 per cent of the lungs of infants surviving birth for five weeks or less contained significant amounts of débris ascribable to fetal aspiration of amniotic contents, although 88 per cent showed at least a few desquamated epithelial cells. It is doubtful if as high a percentage of healthy infants have to cope with birth condtions such as were encountered in those living but a short time.

Other evidence concerning fetal aspiration has been presented recently.[9] Without using an anesthetic a thin hypodermic needle was passed through the abdominal wall and into the amniotic sacs of guinea pig fetuses in the last week or two of gestation. Small quantities of fluid were withdrawn (0.4 cc. to 1 cc.) from the region about the nostrils and replaced with colloidal solutions of thorium dioxide (thorotrast) or hydroxide (thorad). In 27 fetuses so treated a large series of x-ray films exposed after various intervals up to 14 days failed to show lung shadows which would signify that the fetuses had aspirated this opaque material. The thorotrast or thorad was observed in the stomach and intestines, for swallowing occurred regularly.

Twenty-five additional experiments were performed. Films exposed after these injections showed no aspiration on the part of the fetuses. The pregnant guinea pigs were then allowed to breathe atmospheres low in oxygen or high in carbon dioxide or to rebreathe air until an anoxemia was set up. Some of the fetuses could be seen executing rhythmical movements resembling respiration. Roentgenograms were obtained subsequently. Of 14 experiments showing shallow, questionable or no fetal respiratory movements, only two films revealed thorotrast in the fetal respiratory tract. In the remaining 12, all showing strong movements of the type in question, seven positive results such as are illustrated in Fig. 37 were obtained.

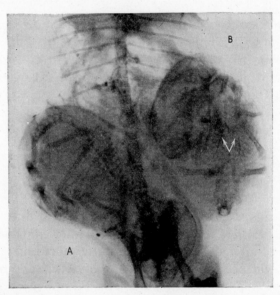

Fig. 37.—Thorotrast (0.8 cc.) injected into the amniotic sacs of two guinea pig fetuses on the 63rd day of gestation. The mother was rendered cyanotic with nitrogen containing a small amount of oxygen. Respiratory movements were observed in fetus B more clearly than in fetus A. Half an hour later, the roentgenogram was made. The bronchial tree of fetus B is well filled with thorotrast (arrows). (Windle, et al.: Surg. Gyn. & Obst., Vol. 69, 1939.)

In addition to these experiments, three other fetuses dying in utero when the mothers died during difficult labor or which were otherwise asphyxiated at the time of birth showed lungs filled with the thorotrast in consequence of having aspirated the amniotic contents (Fig. 38).

The literature contains a report of a human fetus of the 6th month in which an experiment similar to those in the guinea pigs was performed. Ehrhardt[56] placed thorotrast in the amniotic sac 15 hours before he performed an hysterectomy in a mentally defective woman requiring sterilization. Roentgenograms of the fetus taken afterward showed that the thorotrast was concentrated in the stomach and small intestine, but none was present in the respiratory tract. A number of other observations in human fetuses at term, following the use of strontium iodide according to a method devised to outline the fetal position, likewise failed to show fetal lung shadows.[57] However, this material gives a very weak visualization of fetal structures at best. Other experiments

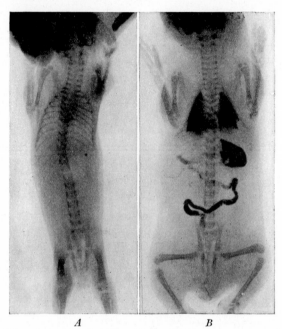

A   *B*

Fig. 38.—Thorotrast (1 cc.) injected into the amniotic sacs on the 61st day of gestation without using anesthesia. Daily roentgenograms showed no lung shadows. Birth occurred on the 64th day. Fetus *A* was alive at birth. Fetus *B* died during birth; its lungs became filled with thorotrast. (Windle, et al.: Surg. Gyn. & Obst., Vol. 69, 1939.)

employing thorotrast, which have been described recently, seem to indicate that human fetuses of 4 to 6 months of gestation do aspirate amniotic fluid in utero.[58] The total number of experiments performed was not stated but one particularly impressive one was described as illustrative of the series. In this instance (5 to 6 months) 25 cc. of thorotrast was injected into the amniotic sac 48 hours before the pregnancy was to be terminated surgically. After 30 hours two films were exposed and these showed rather indefinite shadows which were probably cast by the opaque material aspirated by the fetus. After the operation had been performed roentgenograms of the fetus showed very heavy lung shadows. In these experiments one cannot be certain that physiologically normal conditions prevailed because no specific data were given. The patients required surgical interruption of pregnancy, but it is not known whether they were tuberculous, suffered from cardiac disease, or from some uterine pathology which could have disturbed the normal uterine physiology. Ehrhardt's one patient was a mental defective and presumably had no pathology which would embarrass respiratory exchange in the placenta; correlatively he found no aspiration of amniotic contents. In the more recent experiments there was no mention of preoperative medication and anesthetic.

The experimental studies in guinea pigs demonstrated that aspiration of amniotic contents does not occur normally but that it may be brought about under asphyxial conditions. Furthermore, not all fetal movements which appear to be rhythmical and resemble respiration serve to bring about aspiration of amniotic fluid. The recent human experiments which show aspiration in utero are unimpressive and open to question because proof that they represent the normal condition is lacking. Although minor, atonic respiratory movements may occur during prenatal life, there can be little doubt that the presence of vernix caseosa, lanugo hair, etc. in the lungs of infants at birth is unphysiologic and is associated with the deeper, dyspneic respiratory activity like that encountered in fetuses suffering from rather severe anoxemia.

FETAL HICCUP

The phenomenon of hiccup in utero was first described in 1880 by Mermann[59] and has been observed infrequently by many obstetricians since that time. DeLee[60] reported that hiccups can be identified as early as the fifth month. They are short quick jerks of the shoulders and trunk occurring about 15 to 30 times a minute and are regular (rhythmical?), visible, audible and palpable to the observer. In one instance, he declared, the hiccups were heard just before birth and within a minute after birth the infant was hiccuping so loudly it could be heard in the adjoining room.

In our experience with fetuses of cats and other animals fetal hiccups have never been identified and to my knowledge no other investigators have found them except in the human. However, certain "jerky" movements of the head and trunk, not distinctly of a respiratory nature, may be comparable with the hiccups of the human fetus.

SUMMARY

Consideration of the recent experiments in fetal respiratory movements leads to a more rational conception of the subject than was formerly held. The physiology of respiration in utero is not so greatly different from that of the newborn or even of the adult organism as it might seem.

Early in embryonic life, at a time which varies somewhat in different species, but roughly at about the 10 mm. stage, the part of the somatic motor system which is to be concerned with breathing later on has its genesis. Soon higher neurons are formed and brought into a mutually integrated aggregate to comprise a respiratory center connected with the somatic motor system. Appropriate stimulation by neuronal afferent discharge into the center, by the chemical agent carbon dioxide acting upon it directly or by anoxial depression of its threshold can bring it into activity prematurely; but it is doubtful if this newly formed respiratory mechanism actually functions in the strictly normal course of early intrauterine existence. The respiratory mechanism seems to be a dormant system charged with potentialities long in advance of the time it can be of any use to the fetus.

This period of preparedness varies greatly in different animals. It must be exceedingly brief in the marsupials. Forty-five per cent of the gestation period passes in the cat before respiratory efforts can be induced. The figures are about 30 per cent for man and little more than 25 per cent for the sheep.

It is possible to remove a fetus from the uterus and leave its circulation to the placenta intact, but it is impossible to maintain physiologic conditions comparable to those in utero before the experiment for very many minutes after this has been done. Partial anoxemia sets in promptly, the fetal respiratory center threshold drops and its neurons begin to discharge in response to the usual factors which are stimulatory in adult organisms.

Rhythms of shallow, rapid respiratory movements which are

occasionally encountered in human fetuses late in the gestation period and which have been seen in a few laboratory animals at infrequent intervals signify that the fetus is momentarily experiencing either a depression of the threshold of its respiratory center or an elevation of the carbon dioxide in blood going to the brain. One is justified in postulating a physiologic partial anoxemia in late fetal life associated with progressive decline in placental efficiency and with this, minor rhythms of respiratory movements. Nevertheless, even these minor rhythms of shallow, rapid respiratory movements are not often encountered and when seen should give cause for apprehensiveness on the part of the obstetrician, for the danger of aspiration of amniotic contents then may become real if the partial anoxemia becomes a true asphyxia.

That aspiration is not commonly encountered depends upon the fact that normally the fetus never suffers a truly asphyxial state before it is born. It seems probable that the blood which it receives from the placenta is highly saturated with oxygen throughout the greater part of life in utero. If the oxygen saturation drops into the neighborhood of 50 per cent it is to be expected that shallow, rapid movements of the respiratory muscles will be manifested. These are not accompanied by any changes in intrathoracic pressure because the normal hypotonicity of fetal muscles remains unchanged; consequently no aspiration results. But should the oxygen saturation decrease markedly, numerous motor neurons are activated, muscles tonus increases and dyspneic gasping movements ensue. These bring about aspiration of amniotic contents. One can not doubt however that the fetus possesses a wide margin of safety in respect to the danger of "drowning" in its amniotic fluid.

REFERENCES CITED

1. Preyer, W. 1885. Specielle Physiologie des Embryo., Grieben, Leipzig.
2. Windle, W. F., C. A. Dragstedt, D. E. Murray & R. R. Greene. 1938. Surg. Gynec. Obst., 66: 987.
3. Hartman, C. G. 1920. Anat. Rec., 19: 251.
4. Ahlfeld, F. 1888. Verhandl. deutsch. Gesellsch. Gynäk., 2: 203.
5. Weber, H. 1888. Inaugural dissertation, Marburg. (Cited by Ahlfeld.)
6. Ahlfeld, F. 1905. Monatschr. Geburtsh. Gynäk., 21: 143.
7. Reifferscheid, K. 1911. Pflüger's Arch., 140: 1.
8. Snyder, F. F. & M. Rosenfeld. 1937. J.A.M.A., 108: 1946.

9. Windle, W. F., R. F. Becker, E. E. Barth & M. D. Schulz. 1939. Surg. Gyn. Obst., 69: 705.

10. Corey, E. L.: 1932. J. Exp. Zool., 61: 1.

11. Carmichael, L. 1934. Genetic Psychol. Monogr., 16: 337.

12. Snyder, F. F. & M. Rosenfeld. 1937. Am. J. Physiol., 119: 153.

13. Barcroft, J. & D. H. Barron. 1936. J. Physiol., 88: 56.

14. Barcroft, J. & D. H. Barron. 1937. Ibid., 91: 329.

15. Bonar, B. E., C. M. Blumenfeld & C. Fenning. 1938. Am. J. Dis. Child., 55: 1.

16. Brown, T. G. 1915. J. Physiol., 49: 208.

17. Coronios, J. D. 1933. Genetic Psychol. Monogr., 14: 283.

18. Windle, W. F., M. Monnier & A. G. Steele. 1938. Physiol. Zool., 11: 425.

19. Erbkam. 1837. Neue Ztschr. Geburtsk., 5: 324.

20. Strassmann, P. 1903. Samml. klin. Vortr., Gynäk., No. 132: 947.

21. Minkowski, M. 1922. Schweitzer med. Wchnschr., No. 29 and 30: 721, 751.

22. Bolaffio, M. & G. Artom. 1924. Arch. di Sci. Biol., 5: 457.

23. Walz, W. 1922. Monatschr. Geburtsh. Gynäk., 60: 331.

24. Barcroft, J., D. H. Barron, K. Kramer & G. A. Millikan. 1937. J. Physiol., 90: 29 P.

25. Abel, S. & W. F. Windle. 1939. Anat. Rec., 75: 451.

26. Boucek, C. M. & A. D. Renton. 1931. Surg. Gyn. Obst., 52: 841.

27. Rosenfeld, M. & F. F. Snyder. 1939. Am. J. Obst. & Gyn., 38: 424.

28. Koff, A. K. & M. E. Davis. 1937. Ibid., 34: 26.

29. Cohnstein, J. & N. Zuntz. 1884. Pflüger's Arch., 34: 173.

30. Huggett, A. St. G. 1930. J. Physiol., 69: 144.

31. Barcroft, J. 1935. Irish J. Med. Sci., Series 7; 1: 289.

32. Flint, A. 1880. Am. J. Med. Sci., 80: 69.

33. Salmi, T. 1933. Acta Soc. Med. Fennicae (Ser. B, fasc. 1, art. 2), 18: 1.

34. Zuntz, N. 1877. Pflüger's Arch., 14: 605.

35. Steele, A. G. & W. F. Windle. 1939. J. Physiol., 94: 531.

36. Barcroft, J. and M. F. Mason. 1938. Ibid., 93: 22 P.

37. Barcroft, J., K. Kramer & G. A. Millikan. 1939. Ibid., 94: 571.

38. Eastman, N. J., E. M. K. Geiling & A. M. DeLawder. 1933. Johns Hopkins Hosp. Bull., 53: 246.

39. Eastman, N. J. 1930. Ibid., 47: 221.

40. Bidone, M. 1931. Ann. di ostet. e ginec., 53: 197.

41. Roos, J. & C. Romijn. 1938. J. Physiol., 92: 249.

42. Windle, W. F. and J. Barcroft. 1938. Am. J. Physiol., 121: 684.

43. Windle, W. F., L. G. Scharpenberg & A. G. Steele. 1938. Ibid., 121: 692.

44. Windle, W. F. & D. Nelson. 1938. Ibid., 121: 700.

45. Kuo, Z. Y. & T. C. Shen. 1937. J. Comp. Psychol., 24: 49.

46. Romijn, C. & J. Roos. 1938. J. Physiol., 94: 365.

47. Windle, W. F. 1934. J. Comp. Neur., 59: 487.

48. Windle, W. F., D. W. Orr & W. L. Minear. 1934. Physiol. Zool., 7: 600.

49. Pitts, R. F., H. W. Magoun & S. W. Ranson. 1939. Am. J. Physiol., 126: 673, 689.

50. Henderson, Y. 1938. Adventures in Respiration. Williams & Wilkins, Baltimore.

51. Krafka, J. 1933. Am. J. Dis. Child., 45: 1007.

7

52. Geyl, A. 1880. Arch. Gynäk., 15: 385.
53. Wislocki, G. B. 1920. Contr. Emb., 11: 47.
54. Benecke, E. 1938. Beitr. path. Anat. allgem. Path. 100: 515.
55. Farber, S. & L. K. Sweet. 1931. Am. J. Dis. Child., 42: 1372.
56. Ehrhardt, K. 1937. Münch. med. Wchnschr., 84: 1699.
57. Menees, T. O., J. D. Miller & L. E. Holly. 1930. Am. J. Roent. Rad. Ther., 24: 363.
58. Reifferscheid, W. & R. Schmiemann. 1939. Zentralbl. Gynäk., 63: 146.
59. Mermann, A. 1880. Zentralbl. Gynäk., 4: 377.
60. DeLee, J. B. 1938. The Principles and Practice of Obstetrics, Saunders, Philadelphia.

CHAPTER VII

THE FETAL DIGESTIVE SYSTEM

As we find elsewhere in studying the nature of vital activities before birth the new individual is prepared for postnatal functions far in advance of the time of need. Nowhere is this better illustrated than in the digestive system. Motor activities associated with obtaining and assimilating food are present in prematurely delivered human infants and in late fetal life of many other animals. The digestive secretions appear to be supplied at this time although information concerning them is meager. On the other hand much has been learned about fetal swallowing and gastro-intestinal movements in recent years.

FETAL SWALLOWING

That amniotic fluid is swallowed by the fetus and that it may even serve some useful function during intrauterine life is not a new idea. Preyer[1] summarized the view held in 1885 when he wrote: "That amniotic fluid is a food for the fetus is certain but if it is not swallowed plentifully it contributes little to nourishment beyond mere water feeding." Swallowing was inferred because of the presence of squamous epithelial cells, lanugo hair and vernix caseosa in the digestive tract before birth.

Preyer reviewed experiments which had been performed to determine the source of amniotic fluid but which incidentally provided some evidence of fetal swallowing. Certain chemicals administered by mouth or by injection into the maternal blood stream appeared later in the amniotic fluid although not in the fetal tissues. However, urine samples collected from the infants after birth often contained these substances. It was assumed that the fetus had swallowed the amniotic fluid.[2-5]

Others have demonstrated that rabbit and dog fetuses swallow actively and that absorption of the swallowed fluid takes place readily through the gastric and intestinal epithelia.[6] Two or three hours after injecting calcium ferrocyanide into the amniotic

99

cavity it was possible to induce the prussian blue reaction in all the fetal tissues, especially in the stomach, intestines, kidneys and skin. More recently injections of colloidal dyes into the amniotic cavity in guinea pigs and cats have demonstrated that absorption takes place through the gastro-intestinal mucosa and respiratory epithelium as well as through the amnion itself.[7] Although one must conclude that the fetuses did swallow the amniotic fluid it was not proved that swallowing is a normal physiologic function of the fetus. The experiments were conducted under general anesthesia and under conditions which may have caused a certain amount of anoxemia in the fetuses which in turn could have induced the swallowing.

An ingenious method for treating patients suffering from the effects of the distention of the abdomen attendant upon polyhydramnios has been described.[8] The fetus was apparently induced to swallow more actively by sweetening the amniotic fluid. This was accomplished under local anesthesia by injecting saccharine solution directly through the maternal abdomen into the amniotic cavity. Girth of the abdomen diminished, the disagreeable symptoms of the mother gradually subsided and normal infants were borne by all but one patient. In this one instance in which treatment had been ineffective the child was born alive but a congenital atresia of the esophagus had prevented it from swallowing its amniotic fluid. Polyhydramnios associated with teratoma of the neck which occluded the esophagus has been reported by others.[9]

In the experiments described above saccharine was present in the umbilical vein blood and in the first urine of the infants which had swallowed it. Moreover, by catheterizing the mothers and collecting urine samples regularly after injecting methylene blue together with saccharine it was possible to obtain evidence that the fetus swallowed intermittently. The patients reported an increased incidence of fetal movements at times coinciding with the appearance of dye in their urine. The conclusion reached was that the child apparently sleeps for many hours in utero and, becoming wakeful, begins to move and drink the sweet amniotic fluid.

Other evidence of fetal swallowing in humans has been obtained by injecting materials impervious to x-rays into the amniotic sac after withdrawing an amount of fluid equal to that injected. The first investigators[10] to pursue this type of experimentation used solutions of strontium iodide which were swallowed by the fetus near term. Others have employed "diodrast." [11] Much more striking results have been obtained recently in specimens of five and six months' gestation by means of "thorotrast." [12, 13] Very clear shadows of the fetal stomach were seen in recent

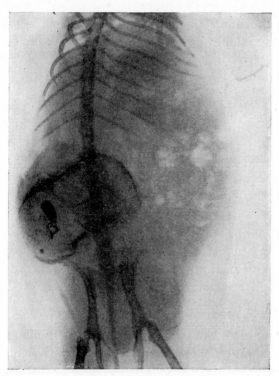

Fig. 39.—Pregnant guinea pig on the 48th day of gestation. Colloidal thorium hydroxide (0.6 cc.) was injected into one amniotic sac on the 46th day; some of it has been swallowed and is in the stomach and intestines. (Becker, et al.: Surg. Gyn. & Obst., Vol. 70, 1940.)

roentgenograms of the uterus and its contents taken after hysterectomy 15 hours or more following injections. From the experiments employing direct injection into the amnion we may conclude that the human fetus can swallow its amniotic fluid at least as early as the 5th month. How much earlier is not known.

Swallowing and gastrointestinal activity have been studied from the developmental standpoint in the guinea pig.[14] Colloidal solutions of non-absorbable and relatively inert thorium dioxide (thorotrast) and thorium hydroxide (thorad) were injected through the intact abdominal wall into the amniotic cavity in small amounts (0.6 cc. to 1.0 cc.) after withdrawing equivalent volumes of amniotic fluid at various times during the gestation period. No anesthesia was used, no surgical procedures were necessary and it was therefore possible to maintain practically normal physiologic conditions. The guinea pig fetuses began to swallow the thorium compounds mixed with amniotic fluid about the forty-second day of gestation, for at that time the first stomach shadows appeared in roentgenograms. Such a shadow can be seen in Fig. 39, a roentgenogram taken on the 48th day. The rapidity with which the material reached the fetal stomach increased with age, taking about 36 hours at 42 days but only about 2 hours in fetuses near term (66 to 67 days). So much fluid was drunk that all the thorium dioxide or hydroxide was flushed out of the amniotic cavity. It took nearly 4½ days for this to be accomplished in the early part of the 3rd quarter of fetal life but only about 18 hours near term. Fetal swallowing seemed to be increased when the mother guinea pigs were subjected to conditions of anoxemia for brief intervals. That swallowing begins at about the time the fetus is growing most rapidly was apparent. The relation of this function to absorption and possibly to fetal water utilization will be discussed later.

FETAL GASTRIC MOTILITY

Movement of the stomach musculature of human fetuses may be implied from the presence of amniotic constituents in the intestines as early as the 4th or 5th month. Furthermore, several investigators have observed gastric motility directly in mammalian fetuses but the extent to which asphyxia occasioned by the experimental procedures induced or influenced the movements is not known.[15, 16] Cat fetuses delivered with placental circulation intact, but of course not functioning as efficiently as normally, showed marked peristaltic movements of the stomach by about the middle of prenatal life, at which time they were only 35 mm. long.[17] After they had grown to 70 mm. the behavior of the stomach appeared to be no different from that in unanesthetized kittens a day or two old (120–140 mm.). Peristalsis was very active and rhythmical, began on the fundic side of the pyloric antrum and spread over the pylorus. Emptying of the stomach contents into the duodenum could be seen, especially when the specimens were allowed to swallow a little air.

X-ray studies in guinea pigs have revealed gastric movements in a few of the fetuses.[14] Furthermore, it was found that stomach emptying time decreased greatly between the 42nd day and the time of birth. Experiments in incubating chicks substantiate these observations.[18] By injecting lycopodium powder into the amnion at various times and examining stomach and intestinal contents later, it was found that swallowing began about the 9th day and it took 10 hours for the material to reach the intestines. At 12 days it required 8 hours and at 16 days, only 2 hours.

Rhythmical waves of movement directed toward the cardiac end of the stomach have been observed in cat fetuses at hysterotomy on a number of occasions.[19] We have seen regurgitation of stomach contents and even of bile colored fluid in cat fetuses during the last third of prenatal life. This seemed to be associated with strong respiratory efforts and perhaps it was caused by compression of the stomach by the abdominal muscle contractions.

Hunger contractions have been studied in newborn infants and in puppies delivered 8 to 10 days prematurely.[20] They were found to be vigorous and more frequent than in the adult.

FETAL INTESTINAL MOVEMENTS

Some of the earliest experiments in fetal intestinal activity are those of Preyer, reviewed in his book in 1885. Between that time and the present only one systematic developmental study has been made. Yanase[21, 22] described intestinal movements which he observed in freshly killed fetuses of the guinea pig and human. He saw the earliest peristalsis in guinea pigs on about the 26th or 27th day (19 mm. long) at which time the longitudinal muscle of the intestine had been laid down. Earlier (15 mm.) only circular muscle was present and he could elicit only local constrictions by pinching and by faradic stimulation. Peristalsis could not be observed in human fetuses before the 11th week although longitudinal muscle and its nerves had been present since the 7th week. Faradic stimulation elicited local contractions during the 6th week when the circular layer alone was present. It was believed that the early intestinal movements were of neurogenic origin. Yanase's observations tell us little about what actually takes place in the normal fetus in utero because he studied asphyxiated material.

We have examined cat fetuses delivered by hysterotomy with placental circulation intact.[17, 19] The cats had been decerebrated previously by the anemia method and required no anesthetic dur-

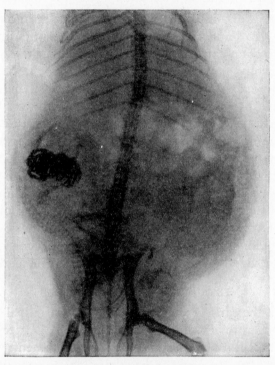

Fig. 40.—Same guinea pig on the 57th day of gestation. Most of the thorium hydroxide has been swallowed, has passed out of the stomach and is concentrated in the intestines. Intestinal constrictions indicating activity can be seen. (Becker, et al.: Surg. Gyn. & Obst., Vol. 70, 1940.)

ing the experiments with their fetuses. Local constrictions of the intestinal wall were induced in embryos 18.5 mm. long (about 1 gram) by mechanical and faradic stimulation. Movements appeared spontaneously upon opening the abdomens of 25 to 35 mm. specimens (2–3 gms.) at about the middle of the gestation period. There seemed to be no well established directional control of the early gut movements. Frequently waves of contraction progressed both orally and aborally from one point of con-striction. Sometimes a movement passed in one direction around a loop of intestine and then reversed itself. Strength of move-ments increased rapidly after midfetal life and by 70 mm. (18 grams) the behavior of the intestine was very much like that seen in unanesthetized kittens a day or two old (110–120 gms.). Po-larity became better established with advancement in age.

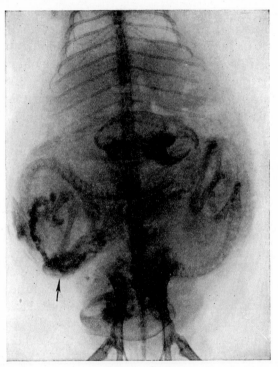

Fig. 41.—Same guinea pig on the day of birth. Defecation in amnio is occur-ring; a pool of meconium is seen in the amniotic sac at the arrow. (Becker, et al.: Surg. Gyn. & Obst., Vol. 70, 1940.)

Intestinal peristalsis of the digestive type involved segmenta-tion and propagation of contents. In some instances spastic rhythmical segmentation of the intestine replaced the digestive type of movement. All specimens were studied under conditions involving a certain amount of anoxemia even though the placentas were intact. It was found that digestive peristalsis tended to prevail when the umbilical vein blood contained on the average

6.5 volumes of oxygen per 100 cc. and that when this decreased to about 2.1 volumes per cent the rhythmical segmentations were more apt to occur. When the fetuses were deeply asphyxiated some time after clamping the umbilical cord, tonus of intestinal musculature diminished and agonal, pendulous writhing movements were manifested. Similar changes in activity of the intestines were observed under profound asphyxia in kittens one or two days old.

It would appear from the roentgenologic study in the guinea pig[14] that intestinal peristalsis is a perfectly normal function of the fetus, but its incidence before swallowing occurs has not been proved in the intact animal. The rate of passage of material along the fetal intestine increases with age. Near term it took only one-fifth the time necessary early in the third prenatal quarter for material to pass from stomach to large intestine. The x-ray films demonstrated segmentations of the intestines very clearly and it was possible to determine that they are more vigorous in late fetal life than they are earlier. Movement of intestinal contents will be seen in Figs. 40 and 41.

ABSORPTION IN THE FETAL DIGESTIVE TRACT

That absorption of chemicals and dyes can occur throughout the gastrointestinal tract of mammalian fetuses was well established by the experiments to which reference was made on page 99.[6, 7] It was proved by the x-ray studies of guinea pig fetuses that large quantities of fluid from the amniotic sac are actually absorbed under normal physiologic conditions.[14] Only a small amount of thorotrast or thorad, usually less than 0.8 cc., was added to many times its volume of amniotic fluid with which it mixed thoroughly. After having been swallowed this dilute solution became concentrated in the stomach and intestines until it cast a dark shadow of these organs. In roentgenograms of one human experiment at 6 months of gestation,[12] it may be seen that a high degree of concentration had been effected in the stomach alone in 15 hours time, for little material passed into the small intestine and yet the amniotic sac was nearly clear. Others[6] have suggested that much of the absorption takes place in the fetal stomach and our own experiments bear this out. Material traverses the duodenum so rapidly that little absorption can occur there; but other parts of the small and especially the large bowel retain their contents for long periods during prenatal life. Considerable absorption undoubtedly takes place in them.

The significance of fetal swallowing, gastrointestinal movements and absorption is not entirely clear. It has been suggested however that these activities serve an important function in fetal life. Some of the water may be of real use to the fetus. Reynolds[23] has shown that the volume of fetal fluid reaches a peak at about the 24th day of gestation in the rabbit and then drops off rapidly until birth, which occurs on the 32nd day. At the time the fluids begin to diminish precipitously the fetal growth curve is rising rapidly. Concurrently, placental growth rate and efficiency of maternal blood flow through the placenta are declining. These facts suggest that some of the water needed for metabolism begins to be taken by mouth from the amniotic reservoir at this point and that during further growth the fetus draws more and more upon this source as it becomes less easy to get sufficient fluids from the placental blood stream. This concept was suggested by Dr. Reynolds who, however, has pointed out that complete occlusion of the human fetal esophagus is not necessarily accompanied by polyhydramnios. There are not enough data on the guinea pig[24, 25] to allow accurate comparison with the rabbit. Fetal growth does begin to increase rapidly about the time (42nd day) swallowing can be demonstrated. Until approximately the 46th or 48th days the volume of amniotic fluid increases steadily. Thereafter conflicting data are encountered.

DEFECATION AND MECONIOPHAGY IN AMNIO

The contents of the fetal intestines are derived from the amniotic fluid swallowed by the fetus, from various secretory products and from desquamated epithelium, both external and internal. They form a dark greenish, viscid, odorless substance passed from the bowel at birth, to which the name meconium has been given. The green color is due largely to the presence of bile pigments and has been reported to be lacking in rare cases of congenital obliteration of the bile ducts, meconium being then light gray or yellow instead of green. Meconium is regularly observed in the fifth month and we have seen it as early as the fourth. It is of lighter color than in later months because biliverdin is not formed in significant amount before the sixth month.[26]

Concerning defecation in amnio there are few observations save our recent ones. Some[26] hold that it occurs occasionally in the human fetus before birth. Meconium is passed at birth or soon thereafter, but the amniotic fluid is usually said to be clear except after prolonged labor or in cases of asphyxia neonatorum. Some evidence has been presented that passage of meconium at birth is due to an increase in the carbon dioxide tension consequent upon lowering of the blood pH and not to a simple accumulation of carbon dioxide.[27] Perhaps it may be related to the establishment of a general visceral motor hyperactivity like that which closes the ductus arteriosus and starts splenic contractions. Although active peristalsis was commonly seen in the large intestine of cat fetuses with placental circulation intact[19] the act of defecation was never observed while the intestines were exposed. The passage of meconium by intact cat fetuses has been seen in a few instances. The amniotic fluid of many species of animals is found to contain meconium after anesthesia has been used. It has been observed at the time of hysterotomy under local anesthesia in human fetuses of 4 months gestation.

Defecation in amnio is a normal physiologic activity in the mature fetus of the guinea pig, occurring about a week before term. Furthermore, the x-ray studies demonstrate that meconium mixes with the amniotic fluid and is swallowed by the fetus.[14] The same material passes through the gastrointestinal tract again and again during the last week of prenatal life. Defecation in amnio on the last day of gestation is illustrated in Fig. 41. Meconiophagy has not been observed in man.

THE FETAL DIGESTIVE GLANDS; ENZYMES

The subject of functional activity in prenatal digestive glands is poorly understood in spite of the fact that many investigators have discussed it. For the most part experiments have been uncontrolled, methods inadequate and results discordant and confused. For a more complete review of the principal studies on enzymes in the various portions of the gastrointestinal tract the reader is referred elsewhere.[29]

Secretion of the salivary glands has been studied extensively at the time of birth, but little is known about their prenatal function. Ptyalin has been identified as early as the fourth month in the human fetus. Mucous glands develop later than serous and contribute little secretion to the saliva of the newborn infant. The nervous mechanism for salivary secretion seems to be at least partially in order at birth.

Lack of agreement concerning presence or absence of hydrochloric acid in the fetal stomach prevails in man as well as in other mammals. The human gastric glands seem to be capable of forming acid about as soon as they differentiate in the fourth month.[30] The presence of free acid has been denied even at the time of birth.[31] Spontaneous secretion appears to be taking place in guinea pig fetuses near term[32] and elaboration of free acid seems to occur in the stomach of rabbit fetuses, the quantity increasing with age.[33]

Several gastric ferments have been identified in the fetal stomach of man and other animals. Pepsin may be present during the fourth or fifth months, rennin appears a little later and amylase has been found at birth. The question whether the fetal stomach actually performs any chemical digestive function or not has been debated. Some have held that the presence of protein curds indicates activity and have made the suggestion that some little nutriment may be gained from the contents of the amnion which are swallowed.[1, 2, 29, 30]

The fetal intestinal glands are said to secrete. Many enzymes have been declared to be present by some investigators and to be absent by others. Maltase, invertase, lactase, erepsin and trypsin have been identified before the fifth month in man; rennin and enterokinase are said to be present by the sixth month and others at full term. The present state of our knowledge is too insecure to justify anything like a complete consideration of intestinal secretions here.[29] However, there is little doubt that the fetal small intestines are prepared for some of the chemical as well as the mechanical digestive processes well in advance of the time they will be called upon to employ them.

The large size of the fetal liver and the fact that it is the only fetal organ which receives undiluted the highly oxygenated blood from the umbilical vein suggests that it performs some important functions before birth. Its hemopoietic rôle in early fetal life has been mentioned in the chapter on fetal blood. Its relationship to prenatal carbohydrate and lipid metabolism will be deferred to the last chapter. It begins its secretory activity early. Between the third and fifth months of gestation the human gall bladder contains a thin mucoid material which is practically colorless, but at about the fifth month the fetal bile begins to take on a yellow appearance. The pigment bilirubin is said to be present at that time and formation of biliverdin is thought to start about a month later.[26] During the last four months of fetal life the bile pigments are produced extensively and the contents of the intestines become deep green in consequence.

The production of bilirubin in the human fetus is related to the commonly encountered pathologic condition known as icterus neonatorum. The mechanism of formation of the pigment and its escape into the blood stream to give rise to hyperbilirubinemia[34] is not understood. Any thorough discussion of this subject would lead us to questions of possible placental function in the capacity of a "uterine liver."[35] Fetal iron metabolism will be considered briefly in the last chapter.

It is well known that the pancreas elaborates secretions in late fetal life. In the calf its proteolytic activity is slight before the fifth or sixth months.[28, 36] Nevertheless some have been able to identify enzymes in the human fetal gland much earlier than this. Trypsinogen, lipase and amylase are present near term and the first two are said to have been detected as early as the fourth month.[29]

REFERENCES CITED

1. Preyer, W. 1885. Specielle Physiologie des Embryo., Grieben, Leipzig.
2. Fehling, H. 1879. Arch. Gynäk., 14: 221.
3. Zuntz, N. 1878. Pflüger's Arch., 16: 548.
4. Wiener, M. 1881. Arch. Gynäk., 17: 24.
5. Krukenberg, G. 1884. Ibid., 22: 1.
6. Wiener, M. 1883. Zentralbl. Gynäk., 7: 409.
7. Wislocki, G. B. 1920. Contr. Emb., 11: 47.
8. De Snoo, K. 1937. Monatschr. Geburtsh. Gynäk., 105: 88.
9. Wilson, J. St. G. 1939. J. Obst. Gyn. Brit. Emp., 46: 44.
10. Menees, T. O., J. D. Miller & L. E. Holly. 1930. Am. J. Roent. Rad. Ther., 24: 363.
11. Case, J. T. 1933. In A. H. Curtis' Obstetrics and Gynecology, 3: 762, Saunders, Philadelphia.
12. Ehrhardt, K. 1937. Münch. med. Wchnschr., 84: 1699.

13. Reifferscheid, W. & R. Schmiemann. 1939. Zentralbl. Gynäk., 63: 146.
14. Becker, R. F., W. F. Windle, E. E. Barth & M. D. Schulz. 1940. Surg. Gyn. Obst., 70: 603.
15. Tani, K. 1927. Jap. J. Obst. Gyn., 10: 2.
16. Friedman, M. H. F. 1936. Proc. Soc. Exper. Biol. & Med., 34: 495.
17. Windle, W. F. & C. L. Bishop. 1939. Ibid., 40: 2.
18. Vrbitch, S. 1924. Compt. Rend. Soc. Biol., 91: 604.
19. Becker, R. F. & W. F. Windle. 1940. Unpublished.
20. Carlson, A. J. & H. Ginsburg. 1915. Am. J. Physiol., 38: 29.
21. Yanase, J. 1907. Pflüger's Arch., 117: 345.
22. Yanase, J. 1907. Ibid., 119: 451.
23. Reynolds, S. R. M. 1939. Physiology of the Uterus, Hoeber, N. Y.
24. Ibsen, H. L. 1928. J. Exp. Zool., 51: 51.
25. Draper, R. L. 1920. Anat. Rec., 18: 369.
26. Feldman, W. M. 1920. Ante-natal and Post-natal Child Physiology, Longmans, Green & Co., London.
27. Noguchi, M. 1937. Jap. J. Obst. Gyn., 20: 248.
28. Ibrahim, J. 1909. Biochem. Ztschr., 22: 24.
29. Needham, J. 1931. Chemical Embryology, Cambridge Univ. Press.
30. Gundobin, N. P. 1912. Die Besonderheiten des Kindersalters, Allgemeine med. Verlags., Berlin.
31. Schmidt, R. 1914. Biochem. Ztschr., 63: 287.
32. Sutherland, G. F. 1921. Am. J. Physiol., 55: 398.
33. Van Puteren, M. 1880. Cited by J. Needham, 1931.
34. Ylppö, A. 1913. Ztschr. Kinderhlk., 9: 208 (1914, Chem. Abst., 8: 941).
35. Schick, B. 1921. Ztschr. Kinderhlk., 27: 231.
36. Banting, F. G. & C. H. Best. 1922. J. Lab. Clin. Med., 7: 464.

CHAPTER VIII

THE FETAL KIDNEYS AND FLUIDS. THE FETAL SKIN

DEVELOPMENT OF KIDNEY FUNCTION

DEVELOPMENT of renal function is related to the formation of amniotic and allantoic fluids so closely that a consideration of one invariably involves the other. The most casual observation in fetuses of laboratory animals reveals the fact that a clear fluid fills the bladder. This is known to be true in human fetuses during the fourth month. Analysis of the bladder contents later in prenatal life demonstrates that the fluid is indeed a dilute urine.[1-3] An appreciable amount of uric acid (100 mg.) was found in the human fetal kidneys at 7 months by one investi-

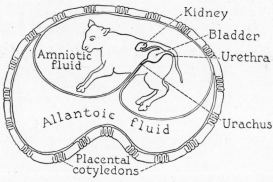

Fig. 42.—Relation of the bladder, amnion and allantois in the fetal calf.

gator.[4] Urea has been detected in human amniotic fluid as early as 2½ months gestation.[5] We may infer from these observations that the fetal kidneys do function, at least to a limited extent, well before they are required to perform all elimination.

Excretion of nitrogenous wastes is accomplished entirely by the fetus in birds. A large allantoic sac is formed to receive the urine, concentrate it and salvage the water which is essential to the fetus for other metabolic processes. The rigid economy of water encountered in birds is not necessary in the mammals. The placenta provides a mechanism for turning over the end-products of fetal metabolism to the maternal blood and kidneys in all the true mammals.   An allantois would seem to be unnecessary but one forms nevertheless, and functions to a variable extent.   The allantois is vestigial in some mammals and man but is exceedingly large in others, opening into the fetal bladder through the urachus.   The urethra communicates with the amniotic vesicle. Thus both allantoic and amniotic fluids can receive the fetal urine.   These relations are illustrated in Figs. 42 and 43.

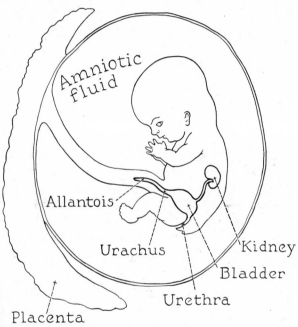

Fig. 43.—Relation of the bladder, amnion and vestigial allantois in the human fetus.

Although the placenta is the chief excretory organ of mammalian fetuses it seems probable that elimination through it varies with the intimacy of the fetal and maternal blood streams. One should not expect the fetal waste products to pass through six tissue layers in the epithelio-chorial placenta of the pig as readily as through only three layers in the hemo-chorial placenta of man or the single membrane which is found in the hemo-endothelial placenta of the higher rodents.   Some believe that there is no placental elimination at all in the pig, sheep and cat, animals in

8

which a large allantois is present.[6]   In general it appears to be true that the species with the simplest placentas are those with the largest allantoic vesicles, and the mammals with highly developed placentas in which the two bloods are more intimately related have very small or vestigial allantoic sacs.

Moreover it has been thought that the size of the embryonic mesonephros is related to the intimacy of the two bloods in the placenta as well as to the development of an allantois.   Bremer[6] found that the trophoblast epithelial layer of the higher placentas becomes thin in certain places and covers the chorionic capillaries like Bowman's capsule invests adult renal glomerular capillaries. He suggested that this formation of trophoblast plates takes place when the mesonephric tubules cease to function and before the true kidney (metanephros) takes over excretion.   He found no trophoblast plates in species whose mesonephric and metanephric function overlapped and concluded that in others the placenta had been forced to adapt itself to more efficient excretory activity in order to bridge a gap in renal function.   However, we shall soon learn that mesonephros and metanephros actually overlap functionally not only in lower mammals but in those with the most efficient placentas as well; the precise relationship just postulated has been questioned.

PHYSIOLOGIC DEVELOPMENT OF THE NEPHRIC TUBULES

There is no lack of evidence that the placenta is the principal excretory organ of the fetus.   It can perform its duties in abnormal fetuses lacking kidneys and in specimens with congenital occlusion of the urinary passages.[7, 8]   Nevertheless, the fact is well established that both mesonephric and metanephric tubules are capable of elimination very early in prenatal life of the normal fetus.

Among the older studies on fetal renal function there are a number in which chemical solutions were injected into the mother and sought in the fetal kidneys or bladder.   Preyer[8] and Needham[1] have reviewed these.   It may be said that placental permeability varies directly with the intimacy of contact between maternal and fetal blood streams and is highest in the hemochorial and hemo-endothelial placentas.   The chemicals used experimentally were recoverable in the fetal urine after introduction into the maternal blood partly because their small molecular size made them capable of passing the placental membranes and the fetal nephric epithelium.

Attempts have been made to inject materials directly into the fetus in order to determine their concentration in the fetal kidney or bladder. A number of experiments in rabbits, cats, guinea pigs and swine have contributed little specific information concerning intrinsic functions of the nephron.[9-13] Chick embryos have been used more extensively than mammals, but it is well known of course that their early nephrons do excrete, for there is no other accessory mechanism like the placenta to function in elimination. Experimental occlusion of the mesonephric (Wolffian) duct leads to hydronephrosis as early as the fourth day of incubation[14] because of pressure of the urine in the mesonephric tubules. Indigo red solutions injected into the vascular systems of chick embryos incubated five days and more[15] appeared in the lumen of the nephric tubules. Trypan blue has been used in the chick by a number of investigators[16-19] and it too made its appearance in the mesonephric and metanephric tubules. Chambers and his colleagues[20, 21] have confirmed and extended these earlier experiments. They found that elimination of phenol red begins in the chick mesonephrons at about 4½ days of incubation. They grew pieces of embryonic kidneys in tissue cultures and used these preparations to study activities of the nephrons. The proximal convoluted tubule of both meso- and metanephrons passed an indicator dye, phenol red, into the lumen and the distal portions of the tubule resorbed water. Some similar experiments have been reported in the duck.[22]

The most significant study of functional capabilities of the mammalian mesonephric and metanephric tubules is that of Gersh[23] who employed carefully controlled histochemical methods. He used a non-toxic solution of sodium ferrocyanide as an indicator of glomerular elimination and phenol red as a test for elimination in the proximal convoluted tubule. These chemicals had been employed previously to study similar functions in adult nephrons.[24] Administration was effected by placental transmission in the rabbit, intravenously in the chick embryo and by direct injection into the fetal bodies (intraperitoneally?) of rabbits, cats, pigs and pouch-young opossums. Results indicate that the ferrocyanide was eliminated with water into the glomerular space from which it passed through the lumen of the remaining portions of the tubules of both mesonephros and metanephros just as in adult kidneys. The phenol red was never found in the glomerular space but did appear in the cells of the proximal part of the tubule and the lumen of the remaining portions in both meso- and metanephros. The criticism may be raised that some dye was passed by the glomerulus but in such a dilution that it could not be detected histologically in the Bowman's capsule. Gersh however considered it doubtful if phenol red was eliminated at all by the glomerulus. Its presence within the cells of the proximal tubules suggested secretion. Concentration of the test substances was sufficiently marked to justify the conclusion that urine was being formed in the mesonephric as well as the metanephric tubules of the embryo.

In all the species studied the mesonephros functioned in eliminating ferrocyanide and phenol red for a shorter or longer time after the metanephric tubules had taken on the same functions. Water resorption in the loop began later than did glomerular and tubular elimination.[23] The high uric acid content encountered in the fetal kidney in one instance suggests that much of the water dialysate together with urea and other soluble compounds which enter the embryonic nephrons is resorbed before reaching the calyces.[4] Fetal nephric excretion appears to be a slow continuous process.

Structural differentiation of the nephric tubule could be correlated with onset of elimination in Gersh's study, but the growth of new blood vessels along the tubules bore no relationship to it. In the glomeruli on the other hand no immediate change in structure appeared to be related to onset of ferrocyanide elimination which, it was suggested, must be due to "some extraglomerular or extrarenal factor such as change in blood pressure, and/or osmotic pressure of the blood colloids or with a submicroscopic change in energy capacity or permeability of the glomerular membrane."[23] The assumption of ability on the part of the kidney to do thermodynamic work is accompanied by increased oxygen consumption as measured by the Warburg method.[25]

That conditions in the human fetal nephrons are similar to those in the other mammals seems certain. Histologically their development is the same. On the basis of differential staining Hewer[26] concluded that an histologic change which may be associated with assumption of functional activity takes place in the convoluted tubules at 12 weeks and possibly as early as 9 weeks. Gersh[23] believes that the human metanephrons begin to eliminate at the 32-mm. stage, which is about 9 weeks fertilization age,[27] and that mesonephric tubules are still functional at that time.

Cameron and Chambers[28] studied tissue cultures of bits of human fetal kidneys at 3½ months. They observed that the cut ends of tubule segments healed over in the cultures, and that phenol red and orange G dye solutions which were present in the culture medium passed into and accumulated in the lumens of the proximal tubules. Furthermore, it was determined that the fluid accumulating in these tubules had a pH of approximately 7.0 while that of the culture medium was from 7.4 to 7.6. In the chick acidification of the cultures with carbon dioxide to a pH of 5.0 failed to prevent the secretion of phenol red.[29]

CONDITIONS REGULATING RENAL FUNCTION

One important deduction made from the experiments with mammalian fetuses is that urine formation is remarkably slow.[23] As a matter of fact it might be considered remarkable that urine is formed at all in fetuses of some species, in which it has been reported that a small gradient between arterial and venous blood pressures exists. In cat fetuses at term arterial pressures of at least 30 mm. and venous pressures somewhat less than 10 mm. of mercury may be physiologic in the large vessels. Filtration in the glomeruli must be carried out at a rather low pressure especially in view of the fact that intraureteral pressure is appreciable.[23] If these observations are correct osmotic pressure of the fetal blood colloids must be low. No information is available in the cat, but it has been found that the osmotic pressure in the dog at birth (with an arterial pressure of 40 mm. mercury) is low.[30]

The protein nitrogen of the dog's blood at birth amounts to 375 mg. per 100 cc. It increases, with a proportional rise in blood pressure, to 800 or 900 mg. in the adult. Each gram of the newborn dog's plasma protein has only about three-fourths the osmotic

equivalent of each gram in the adult. The osmotic pressure of the
fetal blood has not been measured, but in the young puppy it is
16.7 cm. of water when the plasma protein nitrogen concentration reaches 516 mg. per cent, rising to 37.7 cm. of water when the
concentration attains a value of 866 mg. per cent.

In contrast to these data from carnivorous mammals the
gradient between arterial and venous pressures is high in fetal
sheep near term (artery 75 to 80 mm.; vein 18 mm. mercury),
and there is some reason to believe that the osmotic pressure of the
fetal blood is considerably greater than in the dog. The serum
of the sheep fetus has a high proportion of albumin (62 per cent)
and a low proportion of globulin (38 per cent), which would
make the blood protein have, gram for gram, a higher osmotic
pressure than that of the mother. But the total protein content is approximately only about five-eighths that of the mother
per cc. of serum.[31, 32] Consequently the osmotic pressure of the
blood plasma of the sheep fetus may be no higher, if as high, as
that of the mother.

In the human fetus arterial pressures as high as 110 mm. have
been recorded at delivery and the pressure in the veins is no
greater than 20 or 25 mm., perhaps much less under normal conditions within the uterus before labor starts (see Chapter II).
This allows enough of a pressure gradient to account for filtration
in the fetal glomeruli without assuming a reduced osmotic pressure
of the fetal blood colloids. In adult man we know that systemic
arterial pressures greater than 75 mm. and intraureteral pressures
less than 30 mm. of mercury are compatible with urine formation.[33]

In summarizing the present state of our knowledge concerning renal function in prenatal life the following observations appear to be of greatest significance: Excretion begins early in the
true kidney (9 weeks in the human) and is continuous but slow.
The mesonephros functions before the true kidney (metanephros)
and for some time after the latter has taken over urine production.
The fetal glomerulus (capillary tuft and Bowman's capsule) gives
rise to a dialysate from the blood and the rapidity with which
this forms is related to fetal capillary pressure, osmotic pressure of
the fetal blood colloids, carbon dioxide level of the fetal blood
and other factors. Some substances may be contributed to the

glomerular fluid by secretory activity of the cells of the proximal convoluted tubules. Shortly after elimination begins in the glomerulus and proximal tubule, resorption of water and highly soluble compounds occurs in the proximal tubules and the thin segments of Henle's loop in response to an altered osmotic balance in the blood which has passed through the glomeruli. It seems probable that elimination in the fetus can be explained largely on the basis of factors which bring about excretion in the adult, although secretion of tubular epithelium may play a more important rôle in the fetus than in the adult.

The placenta is the chief excretory organ of the human fetus, but its importance appears to vary in other species with the degree of intimacy of the fetal and maternal blood streams. An allantoic vesicle provides a receptacle for fetal urine in some mammals, notably those with the less highly developed types of placentas. The amniotic vesicle can and does receive fetal urine during part of prenatal life in all mammals.

CHANGES IN ELIMINATION AT BIRTH

Provisions are made for rapidly altering many of the organism's vital activities at the time of birth. Changes are encountered in the circulatory and nervous systems and especially in the respiratory mechanism where a sudden shift from placental to lung breathing takes place. It is therefore not surprising to find dramatic structural and functional changes in the kidneys at the time of birth.

High columnar epithelium invests the fetal renal glomerulus. This, the visceral layer of Bowman's capsule, forms a heavy sac which confines the glomerular tufts. Its comparatively low permeability must serve as an impediment to rapid glomerular elimination. The fetus not only does not need a mechanism for rapid filtration in its kidneys, but such a mechanism might actually be detrimental, for it would seriously disturb the fluid balance in utero. When placental elimination is suddenly abolished at birth the columnar epithelial investments of the renal glomeruli burst, allowing the glomerular vascular loops to expand and to come directly into contact with the capsular space. Henceforth glomerular filtration is greatly enhanced.[34]

THE FETAL URINE

Although it has been determined that urine formation is slow nothing is known about the amount produced in any period of time. It is said that the human fetal bladder capacity varies from 40 to 70 cc. between the seventh month and birth.[35] Certainly the amount contained within the bladder at any moment is no measure of the total formed because the amniotic fluid receives an indeterminable quantity.

TABLE 16

CHARACTERISTICS OF HUMAN FETAL URINE

	At term	At term	At 6 months
Freezing point (°)................	−0.141	.....	−0.174
Total N.................gm. %	0.043	0.041	0.061
NaCl..................gm. %	0.136	0.263	0.171

A few chemical analyses have been made on human fetal urine. Makepeace and his colleagues[2] examined samples collected at birth in two specimens and at six months gestation in one other. Jacqué[3] analyzed the bladder urine of fetal sheep 36–47 cm. long and compared the values with adult sheep urine and other fetal fluids. Some of their data appear in Tables 16[1] and 17.

TABLE 17

CHARACTERISTICS OF FLUIDS IN THE SHEEP

	Adult urine	Fetal urine	Allantoic fluid	Amniotic fluid
Freezing point (°).........	−1.959	−0.255	−0.545	−0.470
Protein...........gm. %	.....	0.044	0.054	.....
NaCl.............gm. %	0.22	0.17	0.16	0.64
Total ash........gm. %	0.689	0.37	0.924	0.84
Insol. ash........gm. %	0.13	0.011	0.074	0.017
Sol. ash..........gm. %	0.56	0.34	0.85	0.82

That the contents of the bladder is urine rather than some simple transudate may be assumed from the fact that it is isotonic neither with the blood of the fetus nor with that of the mother; it is low in sodium chloride. Jacqué's data show some resemblance between fetal urine and the allantoic fluid of the sheep, and it may be concluded that the latter is partly concentrated fetal urine.   However, the fetal fluids of the sheep do not contain all the excreted waste products because it is probable that some elimination takes place through the placenta.   The freezing point of the sheep urine decreases after birth; at the end of 36 hours it was $-1.042°$ in one case, in contrast to $-0.255°$ before birth. In other words the hypotonicity of fetal urine in respect to blood (fetal blood $= -0.623°$; maternal sheep blood $= -0.578°$) disappears after birth with the assumption of full elimination by the kidneys.[1]

THE ALLANTOIC FLUID

Few additional facts concerning the allantois and its contents need be mentioned.   The vesicle develops as a ventral diverticulum of the embryonic bladder and maintains a patent connection with the bladder during the first half of fetal life or longer by means of a duct, the urachus.   In those animals with well developed allantois such as the sheep the amount of fluid contained in it rises sharply in early prenatal life, then declines and subsequently increases again toward the end of gestation.   It has a greater volume than the amniotic fluid in early prenatal life and may have more toward the end of gestation in individual cases, but the relationship does not hold throughout the middle of the period when the volume of amniotic fluid overtakes it.   Needham[1] believes, on the basis of the data of a number of other investigators, that there is an exchange of fluids between amnion and allantois (the former giving up fluid to the latter) made possible by the fact that the contents of allantoic and amniotic sacs are separated by nothing more than a double membrane.   The function of the allantois is most clearly indicated in birds where the organ receives all nitrogenous wastes, concentrates and precipitates the uric acid, and salvages the water for other uses.

THE AMNIOTIC FLUID

The most important function performed by the amniotic fluid is the provision of an aquatic environment for the developing embryo.[36]   Were it not for this it is doubtful if uniformly even growth could take place because the very soft embryonic tissues would be molded by pressure from the surrounding structures. The fluid is said also to prevent embryonic adhesions.   Protection from shocks and drying is provided by the chorion, uterus and

body wall more than by the amniotic fluid and the delicate membrane enclosing it.   The fluid-filled amniotic sac acts as an hy-
draulic wedge for the descending fetal head at the time of birth
and helps make fetal postural adjustments to birth possible.

The composition of amniotic fluid has been studied in man
and several other animals[2, 3, 5, 37-39] but a detailed account of its
chemistry would be out of place here.[1]   It has a specific gravity of
about 1.0069[38] in man and is definitely hypotonic both to the
maternal and fetal blood, containing less sodium chloride and
other salts.   Its urea and uric acid content gives a clue to the
origin in part.   The quantity of these two substances increases
during prenatal life, as may be seen in Table 18.[5]   It follows that
the amniotic fluid receives a significant contribution from the
fetal kidneys throughout most of the gestation period.

TABLE 18

CHARACTERISTICS OF HUMAN AMNIOTIC FLUID

Month of gestation	Volume (cc.)	Freezing point (° C.)	Urea (mg. %)	Uric acid (mg. %)
2.5	40	−0.520	34	3.4
4.5	140	−0.515	38	4.0
7.5	1,050	−0.482	40	4.5
10.0	1,800	−0.467	44	5.1

This brings us to the still unsettled controversy regarding
the source and method of formation of amniotic fluid.   Stated in
the simplest terms, two theories have developed: (a) that the fluid
is a transudate or dialysate of the mother, and (b) that it is
formed entirely by the fetus, some investigators holding that it is
a secretory product of fetal kidneys and amniotic epithelium.   A
detailed consideration of all information bearing upon the subject
can not be given here; and once more the reader must turn to
more extensive reviews.[1]

In the sheep, an animal with a large allantois as well as
amnion, it has been found that the fetal urine is passed from the
bladder through the urachus to the allantois (see Fig. 42) up to
a little past the middle of the gestation period.[3]   In late fetal life
however the urethra transmits urine into the amnion and the
urachus ceases to supply it to the allantois.   A mid-interval exists
during which both vesicles receive the fetal urine.

One of the strongest arguments favoring the theory of fetal origin of amniotic fluid is based on experiments of Watson[40] who found that rabbit fetuses died when the amniotic fluid was withdrawn from the pregnant does, but the maternal part of the placenta continued to grow and was vascularized normally. There was no regeneration of the amniotic fluid. Other evidence for at least a partial fetal origin is of course the proved fact of fetal renal activity and the presence of an open pathway from the kidneys to the amniotic space. The presence of fructose and of certain proteins in fetal urine of some species of animals and in the amniotic and allantoic fluids of the same but not in others adds weight to the theory of fetal origin.[41]

It has been pointed out that the chorion of the cat and the vitelline membrane of the rabbit are vascularized by fetal vessels which are interposed between the fetal fluids and uterus. Furthermore, the cat's endometrial epithelium is rather thoroughly restored during the last half of pregnancy except at the placental site. These facts make it seem unlikely that fetal fluids can arise as a transudate from the mother's endometrium to the amniotic sac during the last half of gestation in the cat and rabbit.

Some interesting experiments leading to production of polyhydramnios in rabbits provide rather convincing evidence that the amniotic fluid is formed by fetal structures.[42, 43] After double nephrectomy of pregnant rabbits it was found that a significant increase in amniotic fluid volume occurred during the latter part of the gestation period when the fluid volume is normally decreased. No edema, ascites or other transudate was encountered in the mother's body. Average data from this study are presented in Table 19.[42]

TABLE 19

AVERAGE VOLUMES OF AMNIOTIC FLUID IN RABBITS

Ave. wt. fetus (gms.)	Controls (cc.)	Nephrectomized (cc.)
Less than 10	2.4	.....
10–20	4.9	4.1
20–30	3.3	4.8
30–40	1.7	5.6
40–50	0.5	10.75

Injection of large amounts of saline solution into non-nephrectomized pregnant animals leads to formation of transudates in the mother's body cavities without increasing the amount of amniotic fluid.[44]

Although the strongest evidence favors the concept that amniotic fluid is formed by fetal structures it does not prove that this is its only source in all species. It is certainly not formed entirely by the fetal kidneys. Early in embryonic life before renal function becomes established we do not know its origin. The amniotic epithelium and blood vessels of the embryo have been suggested. The possibility of maternal origin can not be dismissed entirely. More than 200 cc. may be present in the pig when the fetus is only 30 mm. long.[45] Certain chemical compounds, enzymes and antibodies present in the mother's body appear in the placenta and amniotic fluid but not in the fetal tissues themselves.[1]

The quantity of amniotic fluid increases sharply during the early part of prenatal life in all species of animals. In some, such as the cat and guinea pig, the rise has been found to continue to full term, but with considerable individual variation.[45] In others, probably man and the sheep, it attains a maximum some time before the end of gestation and this volume is maintained until term. A remarkable diminution in the quantity of amniotic fluid is encountered in the latter part of prenatal life of the rabbit. A careful comparative study of the minute volume of blood flow in the uterus correlated with the quantity of fetal fluids at different ages may help explain species differences. The great individual and species variations in volume of amniotic fluid seen during late pregnancy may be related in part to the phenomenon of fetal swallowing.[46] It has been reported[47] that polyhydramnios in human subjects can be reduced by stimulating swallowing by the fetus.

THE FETAL SKIN

Little can be said regarding the physiology of the fetal skin and its associated structures. The sweat glands are present and have developed lumens by the seventh month but it is questionable whether they actually secrete in utero. The sebaceous glands do function before birth, adding their oily secretion to desqua-

mated epithelium and lanugo hair to form the vernix caseosa
which covers the fetus. It is usually said that this material serves
to protect the living epithelial cells from becoming macerated in
the amniotic fluid, a statement for which there does not appear to
be the least justification. Others have held on the basis of unsatisfactory evidence that the vernix caseosa is a deposit upon
the skin from lipids excreted by the amnion.[48] The vernix is
usually removed for esthetic reasons at the time of birth, but
when allowed to remain it has been found that it will disappear
of its own accord in about 8 hours,[48] probably by absorption during drying and cornification of the outer epithelial layer.

Other cutaneous glands are capable of functional activity at
birth. A most curious transient phenomenon is encountered
in the mammary glands (see Chapter XIV). A small quantity
of secretion is often observed in both sexes and to this the name
"witch milk" has been applied. Lacrimal glands are well formed
in prenatal life but apparently they do not function. The newborn child is said to cry without tears.

Skin pigmentation is deficient at birth even though melanin
production starts early elsewhere; pigment granules start to form
in the optic cup of the 7 mm. human embryo. Melanin appears
to be manufactured by the fetal tissues with the aid of an oxydase.
Although pigment is not found in the hair primordia of human
fetuses until the fifth month and is not present in the epidermal
cells before the sixth, the enzyme is there earlier and can produce pigment when the dopa reagent (dihydroxyphenylalanine)
is added experimentally.[49] The developmental chemistry of the
skin should be an interesting and profitable study.

The fetal skin can have no importance from the standpoint of
heat regulation in utero, but it is of interest to know whether
or not this function is present at birth. For more than a century
it has been known that the offspring of some animals are incapable of maintaining their birth temperature when removed from
a warm environment.[50] Young rabbits and kittens acquire ability
to fully regulate their temperatures about 15 days after birth.
Other animals, such as the guinea pig, are born with a good coat
of hair and possess a well formed heat regulatory mechanism at
that time. Similar species differences are encountered in birds,
with the chick of the domestic fowl falling into the class of the

guinea pig.[51, 52] Many animals can compensate for a drop in temperature by increasing their metabolism but are incapable of meeting the conditions imposed by a high temperature in the external environment; the rabbit, cat and man are in this class. Others, such as the mouse, possess no form of heat regulation while still others, the guinea pig being an example, are completely homothermic at birth.[53]

REFERENCES CITED

1. Needham, J. 1931. Chemical Embryology, Cambridge Univ. Press.
2. Makepeace, A. W., F. Fremont-Smith, M. E. Dailey & M. P. Carroll. 1931. Surg. Gyn. & Obst., 53: 635.
3. Jacqué, L. 1906. Arch. Internat. Physiol., 3: 463.
4. Lewis, J. H. 1916. J. Biol. Chem., 24: 249.
5. Guthmann, H. & W. May. 1930. Arch. Gynäk., 141: 450.
6. Bremer, J. L. 1916. Am. J. Anat., 19: 179.
7. Englisch, J. 1881. Arch. Kinderhlk., 2: 85.
8. Preyer, W. 1885. Specielle Physiologie des Embryo, Grieben, Leipzig.
9. Bar, P. 1881. Recherches pour servir a l'histoire de l'hydramnios. Paris. (Cited by I. Gersh, 1937.)
10. Fritschek, F. 1928. Ztschr. mik.-anat. Forsch., 13: 61.
11. Firket, J. 1920. Compt. Rend. Soc. Biol., 83: 1230.
12. Wislocki, G. B. 1921. Johns Hopkins Hosp. Bull., 32: 93.
13. Frankenberger, Z. 1921. Rozpravy Ceske Akademie, 30: 47. (Cited by I. Gersh, 1937.)
14. Boyden, E. A. 1924. J. Exp. Zool., 40: 437.
15. Bakounine, S. 1895. Arch. Ital. Biol., 23: 350.
16. Zaretsky, S. 1910. Virchow's Arch., 201: 25.
17. Atwell, W. J. & E. B. Hanan. 1926. Anat. Rec., 32: Suppl. 228.
18. Hurd, M. C. 1928. Am. J. Anat., 42: 155.
19. Wislocki, G. B. 1921. Anat. Rec., 22: 267.
20. Chambers, R. & G. Cameron. 1932. J. Cell. Comp. Physiol., 2: 99.
21. Chambers, R., L. V. Beck & M. Belkin. 1935. Ibid., 6: 425.
22. Sandstrom, C. J. 1935. Anat. Rec., 62: 7.
23. Gersh, I. 1937. Contr. Emb., 26: 33.
24. Gersh, I. 1934. Am. J. Physiol., 108: 355.
25. Flexner, L. B. & I. Gersh. 1937. Contr. Emb., 26: 121.
26. Hewer, E. E. 1924. Quart. J. Exp. Physiol., 14: 49.
27. Altschule, M. D. 1930. Anat. Rec., 46: 81.
28. Cameron, G. & R. Chambers. 1938. Am. J. Physiol., 123: 482.
29. Chambers, R. & R. T. Kempton. 1933. J. Cell. Comp. Physiol., 3: 131.
30. Clark, G. A. & H. E. Holling. 1931. J. Physiol., 73: 305.
31. McCarthy, E. F. 1938. Ibid., 93: 81.
32. Howe, P. E. 1925. Physiol. Rev., 5: 439.
33. Smith, H. W. 1937. The Physiology of the Kidney, Oxford Univ. Press.
34. Gruenwald, P. & H. Popper. 1940. J. Urol., 43: 452.
35. Feldman, W. M. 1920. Ante-natal and Post-natal Child Physiology, Longmans, Green, N. Y.

36. Mossman, H. W. 1937. Contr. Emb., 26: 129.
37. Döderlein, A. 1890. Arch. Gynäk., 37: 141.
38. Uyeno, D. 1919. J. Biol. Chem., 37: 77.
39. Cantarow, A., H. Stuckert & R. C. Davis. 1933. Surg., Gyn. & Obst.,
    57: 63.
40. Watson, B. P. 1906. J. Obst. Gyn. Brit. Emp., 9: 13.
41. Paton, D. N., B. P. Watson & J. Kerr. 1907. Trans. Roy. Soc. Edin.,
    46: 71.
42. Wolff, B. 1904. Arch. Gynäk., 71: 224.
43. Wolff, B. 1909. Ibid., 89: 177.
44. Bakounine, S. 1900. Atti d. r. Accad. med.-chir., Napoli, 54: 1. (Cited
    by J. Needham, 1931.)
45. Wislocki, G. B. 1935. Anat. Rec., 63: 183.
46. Becker, R. F., W. F. Windle, E. E. Barth & M. D. Schulz. 1940. Surg.
    Gyn. & Obst., 70: 603.
47. De Snoo, K. 1937. Monatschr. Geburtsh. Gynäk., 105: 88.
48. Keiffer, H. 1926. Gynec. et Obstét., 14: 1.
49. Bloch, B. 1921. Arch. f. Dermatol. Syphilis, 135: 77.
50. Edwards, F. 1824. Traité de l'influence des agents physiques sur la vie,
    Paris. (Cited by M. S. Pembrey, 1895.)
51. Pembrey, M. S. 1895. J. Physiol., 18: 363.
52. Giaja, J. 1925. Ann. d. Physiol. et Phys.-Chém. Biol., 1: 628. (Cited
    by J. Needham, 1931.)
53. Ginglinger, A. & C. Kayser. 1929. Compt. Rend. Soc. Biol., 101: 711.

CHAPTER IX

THE FETAL MUSCLES

TISSUE CULTURES AND IN-VITRO EXPERIMENTS

HISTOGENESIS of muscle tissue has been carefully investigated[1] and a few observations have been made from the standpoint of function. Although it is difficult to make physiologic studies on the earliest embryonal muscles in vivo, it has been possible to obtain growth from small pieces of muscle in tissue culture and to study the behavior of new cells in this altered environment. Thus, valuable information concerning the activity of very young cells of smooth, cardiac and skeletal muscle has been gained.

At one time discussion centered about the question whether or not muscle tissue can contract in the absence of nerve fibers supplying it. We now know that it can, and it does so under normal physiologic conditions in some locations. For example the amnion of the chick embryo contains sheets of smooth muscle in which nerve fibers have never been demonstrated.[2] This tissue functions actively to churn the embryo about in a rhythmical fashion. Then too, the embryonic heart begins to beat well in advance of the time nerves grow into it. Tissue cultures give conclusive proof that nerves are not essential. Recent histologic studies of amphibian and mammalian heart primordia have demonstrated that specialized cytologic structures, fibrillae, and cross striations, are not formed until after contractility has become well established.[3, 4]

Nerve-free cultures of both cardiac muscle and amniotic smooth muscle from chick embryos demonstrate spontaneous rhythmical contraction in isolated cells as well as in groups of cells.[5, 6] Similarly, pieces from the legs of 4 to 10 day chicks, grown in Lewis-Locke solution, contain functional myoblasts and young skeletal muscle fibers.[7] All these young isolated elements do not contract at any one time and the period of the rhythm varies in different ones, some skeletal fibers contracting as often as 120 times a minute, some in slower rhythms and others only once in one to ten minutes.

Interesting differences have been observed in the nature of the contractions of smooth, cardiac and skeletal muscle cells in tissue cultures. Individual contractions of amniotic smooth muscle cells are slow and seem to be produced by currents of protoplasm flowing toward a center of active change in the cell. This results in a local piling up of the protoplasm at the center of active change. In embryonic cardiac muscle cells the contractions appear as quick rhythmical beats, the cell bellying out at its center with each beat. Individual cells as well as groups showed this phenomenon. Contractions of skeletal muscle fibers and myoblasts resemble straight twitches rather than the flowing and beating movements of the smooth and cardiac elements. In no type of muscle could myofibrils be demonstrated in the living cells.[6] Recent studies have shown that it is impossible to relate the genesis of contractility in rat embryonic skeletal muscle in vivo to any intrinsic structural change in the cell.[8]

The cause of the spontaneous contractions of embryonic muscle cells and myoblasts in cultures is not known, but autochthonicity is not necessarily assumed. Many cells are inactive while one contracts. Activity may depend upon some change in the tissue itself or in the surrounding medium. A certain optimum balance of sodium, potassium and calcium ions (Lewis-Locke solution) has proved to be favorable. Slight changes in this ionic balance and dilution of the medium sometimes stimulates an increase in activity for a brief period but soon leads to degeneration of the growth.

In the amniotic smooth muscle a lack of oxygen or an accumulation of carbon dioxide appeared to bring about cessation of spontaneous rhythmical activity in vitro.[6] This seems to be equally true of adult smooth muscle, although some believe that carbon dioxide may act as a stimulus to rhythmical spontaneous activity.[9, 10] In the intact egg of the chick the amnion becomes progressively more active during the course of incubation until about the 13th day, after which contractions are less frequent. From analyses of the atmosphere within the air-space of the incubating egg[11] we know that cessation of amniotic activity coincides with the time a physiologic partial anoxemia becomes well established.

SPONTANEOUS ACTIVITY OF INTACT SKELETAL MUSCLE

Skeletal muscle fibers and myoblasts begin to develop in 11 mm. to 12 mm. cat embryos about 23 days after insemination. One should expect to encounter functional activity at that time and, to be sure, faradic stimulation with micro-electrodes does result in contractions.[12]   However, spontaneous movements have never been observed in small embryos when studied with their placental circulation intact, and we may conclude that the early skeletal muscle cells possess no autochthonicity in vivo.   Furthermore, removal of the specimens from the uterus with consequent asphyxia does not bring about automatic muscular activity.   Embryos only a little larger than these (13.5 mm.) do show spontaneous movements of the forelimbs under certain unnatural conditions.   When removed from the uterus they remain perfectly inactive so long as the surrounding medium contains sodium, potassium and calcium ions in the proportion found in Locke's solution.   When an ionic unbalance is introduced by substituting solutions deficient in calcium or potassium or both, the forelimbs begin to move rhythmically in a waving manner.[13, 14, 15]   In larger specimens the rhythmical movements occur first in the tail and limbs, structures from which diffusion can take place most readily.   We may conclude that spontaneous contractility of new muscle fibers is stimulated by ionic unbalance in the young tissues.   But since nerve fibers are already present in the intact specimens, one does not know whether the muscle itself responds to direct stimulation, whether the nervous elements are stimulated or whether some elementary nervous inhibitory control over the new muscle has been removed by the change of medium, thus allowing the muscle fibers to exhibit contractility which is their inherent property and which never manifests itself in the presence of nerves.

Small mammalian embryos stand in marked contrast with those of lower vertebrates in respect to the absence of observable contractions of intact skeletal muscles.   Some investigators have reported muscle twitching and even rhythmical contractions before external stimulation elicits responses of a reflex nature.[16]   In some experiments activity of the nervous centers seems to have been excluded, the movements being entirely aneural but occurring only upon direct stimulation.[17, 18]

FARADIC AND MECHANICAL STIMULATION

Development of contraction of skeletal muscles in response to stimulation has been studied in several species of animals. That contractility can be induced before a fetal reflex mechanism can activate it has been well established in mammals.[12, 19–22] The first muscular responses were obtained in cat embryos only 11 mm. long (Fig. 44). These were brought about by faradic stimulation with micro-electrodes applied to points directly over developing muscle masses. The forelimb is scarcely more than a limb bud at this time but it did move outward, forward or backward, depending on the position of the electrodes. These forelimb movements were the first responses which could be obtained. Soon the head could be caused to flex to one side or the other, and at the 12 mm. stage separate movements of the proximal and

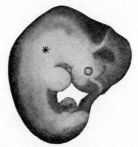

Fig. 44.—Cat embryo 11 mm. C. R. length. The first muscle contractions were elicited by stimulating the region marked with the asterisk (*).

distal parts of the forelimb were induced. At this time contractions of the entire trunk and even the tail muscles appeared. Further development was very rapid and soon a large number of muscles could be brought into activity by properly placed stimuli. It is apparent from these studies that in a general way the course of physiologic development proceeds caudally and rostrally from the shoulder region and distally and ventrally from the dorsal part of the trunk.

Faradic stimuli were more effective than other kinds during the earliest stages of muscle development. Strong mechanical stimuli produced contractions, but they could not be applied with as much finesse and the passive movement brought about by such means made it difficult to see muscle contractions. As development proceeds, the strength of stimulus needed to induce a response decreases.   Several factors other than strength of stimuli determine whether or not responses to direct muscle stimulation will be obtained.   Movements were at their best in specimens whose placental circulation was intact and which had been delivered into a saline bath at body temperature.   Death of the embryo abolished responses only after a considerable length of time.   Contractions of the embryonic muscles persisted after lowering the bath temperatures 10 or 15 degrees Centigrade but were abolished quickly by raising it less than 5 degrees above normal body temperature.

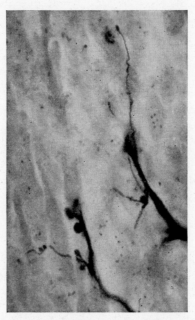

Fig. 45.—Photomicrograph of nerve fibers ending upon myoblasts in the shoulder region of a 7-week human embryo.   Pyridine-silver stain; × 450.

The induced embryonic muscle contractions possess certain characteristics unlike those of reflexes. A minimal stimulus gives rise to a quick, sharp, immediate contraction moving the forelimb, let us say, outward. Upon cessation of the stimulation, the limb tends to maintain this contraction momentarily, returning more slowly to the original position (see "fetal tetanic reaction," below). A second stimulation following closely upon this induces another response, for there appears to be no grossly per-ceptible fatigue period. The direction of movement can be controlled by placing the electrodes in different positions. This indicates that the stimuli were well localized and suggests that rather small groups of muscle fibers were being stimulated. Histologically it was found that a few primitive nerve fiber terminations are already present in the embryonic muscles at the time early contractions can be obtained (Fig. 45). Whether or not these nerve endings have anything to do with the nature of responses to direct stimulation is undetermined.

THE FETAL TETANIC REACTION

A most interesting study of fetal muscle physiology was made by Minkowski[23] who tested the excitability of nerves and of muscles to galvanic and faradic stimulation in 20 human fetuses 15 mm. to 350 mm. crown-heel length after removal from the uterus. By applying galvanic stimuli directly to the muscles, he found only two specimens which did not react. In four others the anodal closing contractions were sharp and were followed by slow, often incomplete relaxation while the current was still passing. Breaking the circuit produced a new sharp contraction. Fourteen fetuses responded to closing the circuit both at the anode and cathode with a quick contraction of the muscle; upon reaching a certain magnitude, they remained contracted so long as the current flowed. There followed a slower relaxation after breaking the circuit. To this phenomenon the name "fetal tetanic reaction" was given. Faradic stimulation, as has been observed in young infra-human fetuses, produced a similar quick contraction followed by a slow relaxation.

Minkowski was not the first to make a study of the electrical responses in fetal muscles but his emphasis of the tetanic reaction was new. Others[24] experimented with human fetuses of about 7 months gestation and reported no tetanic reaction. However, Bichat[25] recognized that skeletal muscles of fetal guinea pigs can be induced to contract in response to electrical stimulation and found that the more mature the fetus, the better and more rapid the reaction. Preyer[19] spoke of tonic contraction of the muscles of rabbit fetuses in which he had stimulated the spinal cord with faradic shocks.

In the newborn rabbit, cat and dog, excitability to electrical stimulation is less than in adults.[26] The muscle of the newborn acts like that of a fatigued animal, as may be seen in Fig. 46. Although it took 70 stimuli to bring about tetanus in the adult, only 16 were required to do so in the newborn, conditions being the same. These studies have been confirmed in human infants.[27, 28]

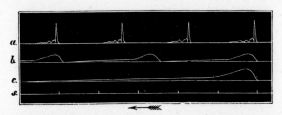

Fig. 46.—Myograms in the cat: *a*, adult; *b*, 7-day-old kitten; *c*, newborn. Time in seconds. Arrow indicates direction of movement of the paper. (Soltmann: Jahrb. Kinderhlk., Vol. 12, 1878.)

The character of the myogram was studied in one healthy premature infant weighing 1,260 grams and comparisons were made with normal newborns and with infants suffering from several diseases.[29] We are interested in the results obtained in the healthy individuals and have reproduced them in the following Table 20.

TABLE 20

CHARACTERISTICS OF MYOGRAMS IN HUMAN INFANTS

Age	Latent period (sigma)	Maximum contraction reached (sigma)	Duration of contraction (sigma)	Height of contraction (mm.)
Premature..........	31.6	61.5	688.9	20.5
3 hours.............	17.2	50.8	393.1	15.0
3 weeks.............	18.3	52.5	304.2	19.0
6 months...........	21.8	58.8	272.3	18.5

It will be seen that the latent period was longer, the contraction a little slower and its duration much greater in the one premature infant than in the newborn; but no significance should be placed on a study of one individual. According to another investigator[30] the latent period of muscle in young rat fetuses is betwen 500 and 1,000 sigma. How this was determined is not stated.

EXCITATION OF FETAL MUSCLE BY NERVE STIMULATION

Fetal muscle responds to direct stimulation, as we have said, in advance of the time it can be activated by stimulating nerves. All investigators agree upon this point. In cat, rat and sheep fetuses, responses to nerve stimulation can be elicited soon after the first direct muscle contractions. In the human it has been reported to be about a month later.[31] Contractions following human nerve stimulation were not obtained until about the fourth month of gestation, at which time the responses were less lively and less constant than those following direct muscle stimulation. They should be manifested much earlier than this.[32] It has been found that asphyxia prejudices the results obtained from stimulation of the nervous system.[33] Since all of the human fetuses were studied under asphyxial conditions it is doubtful if results with indirect activation of the fetal muscles can be of great significance.

The type of motor response obtained by stimulating the spinal motor centers of small cat fetuses differs from that which results from stimulating the muscle itself with faradic shocks. When the point of a fine dental broach is passed into the spinal cord or when a faradic shock is applied to the cord by micro-electrodes the movements which occur are quicker and their tetanic or maintained characteristic is not so pronounced as it is when the muscle itself is stimulated. The direction of movement is less easily molded than it is when the electrodes are shifted about over the surface of muscle masses. Furthermore, fatigue enters in when motor centers are stimulated directly, making a second response difficult to elicit after obtaining the first one.

EFFECTS OF CURARE

Recently an attempt was made to curarize small rat fetuses of 17 days gestation delivered by experimental Caesarean section.[34] It was reported that three minutes after injecting a minute amount of a one per cent solution of this drug, reflexes were abolished but direct muscle stimulation still produced contractions. These results are very different from those obtained 50 years earlier in guinea pig fetuses.[19] At that time it was reported that a dosage adequate to curarize an adult guinea pig in 10 minutes failed to affect the fetuses when injected into them in utero until 52 minutes had elapsed; complete fetal curarization did not come about for 80 minutes. Furthermore, the drug passed through the placental barrier from fetal to maternal side and killed the mother before affecting the fetus. It seems doubtful if the observations on such small fetuses as were used in the recent experiments can mean more than that reflexes had died out because of asphyxial conditions prevailing during the experiments.

FETAL RIGOR MORTIS

There has been discussion from time to time as to whether or not fetuses dying in utero exhibit the phenomenon of rigor mortis. Ballantyne[35] reported several cases and gave references to the early literature on this subject. From what is known of the chemistry and physiology of fetal skeletal muscle there is no reason to doubt that rigor does take place but it may not be as pronounced as in the adult. The phenomenon has been described in kittens dying in utero.[36] In no case was the degree of rigidity as marked in the fetus as in the mother cat.

REFERENCES CITED

1. Arey, L. B. 1940. Developmental Anatomy. 4th ed. Saunders, Philadelphia.
2. Clark, E. L. & E. R. Clark. 1914. J. Exp. Zool., 17: 373.
3. Copenhaver, W. M. 1939. J. Exp. Zool., 80: 193.
4. Goss, C. M. 1940. Anat. Rec., 76: 19.
5. Burrows, M. T. 1912. Münch. med. Wchnschr., 59: 1473.
6. Lewis, Margaret R. 1915. Am. J. Physiol., 38: 153.
7. Lewis, Margaret R. 1920. Contr. Emb., 9: 191.
8. Straus, W. L. 1939. Anat. Rec., 73: Suppl. 50.
9. Hooker, D. R. 1912. Am. J. Physiol., 31: 47.
10. Mansfeld, G. 1921. Pflüger's Arch., 188: 241.
11. Romijn, C. & J. Roos. 1938. J. Physiol., 94: 365.
12. Windle, W. F., D. W. Orr & W. L. Minear. 1934. Physiol. Zool., 7: 600.
13. Angulo y Gonzalez, A. W. 1930. Proc. Soc. Exp. Biol. & Med., 27: 579.
14. Angulo y Gonzalez, A. W. 1934. Anat. Rec., 58: Suppl. 45.
15. Windle, W. F. 1939. Physiol. Zool., 12: 39.
16. Tracy, H. C. 1926. J. Comp. Neur., 40: 253.
17. Wintrebert, P. 1920. Arch. Zool. Exp. Gen., 60: 221.
18. Hooker, D. 1911. J. Exp. Zool., 11: 159.
19. Preyer, W. 1885. Specielle Physiologie des Embryo. Grieben, Leipzig.
20. Angulo y Gonzalez, A. W. 1933. Proc. Soc. Exp. Biol. & Med., 31: 111.
21. Raney, E. T. & L. Carmichael. 1934. J. Genetic Psychol., 45: 3.
22. Barcroft, J., D. H. Barron & W. F. Windle. 1936. J. Physiol., 87: 73.
23. Minkowski, M. 1928. Schw. Arch. Neur. Psychiat., 22: 64.
24. Bolaffio, M. & G. Artom. 1924. Arch. di Sci. Biol., 5: 457.

25. Bichat, X. 1822. General Anatomy. Trans. by G. Hayward, Richardson & Lord, Boston.

26. Soltmann, O. 1878. Jahrb. Kinderhlk., 12: 1.

27. Westphal, C. 1886. Neur. Centralbl., 5: 361.

28. Westphal, A. 1894. Arch. Psychiat., 26: 1.

29. Krasnogorski, N. 1914. Jahrb. Kinderhlk., 79: 261.

30. Angulo y Gonzalez, A. W. 1936. Cited by D. Hooker. Yale J. Biol. & Med., 8: 579.

31. Minkowski, M. 1922. Schw. med. Wchnschr., 52: 721, 751.

32. Windle, W. F. & J. E. Fitzgerald. 1937. J. Comp. Neur., 67: 493.

33. Windle, W. F. & R. F. Becker. 1940. Arch. Neur. Psychiat., 43: 90.

34. Angulo y Gonzalez, A. W. 1935. Proc. Soc. Exp. Biol. & Med., 32: 621.

35. Ballantyne, J. W. 1902. Manual of Antenatal Pathology and Hygiene. The Foetus. William Green & Sons, Edinburgh.

36. Tissot, J. 1894. Arch. physiol. norm. path., Ser. 5, 6: 860.

CHAPTER X

THE GENESIS OF FUNCTION IN THE NERVOUS SYSTEM

THE beginning of functional activity in the nervous system has been investigated most thoroughly in embryos of the rat,[1-4] guinea pig,[5, 6] sheep,[7, 8] and cat,[9-13] and less completely in man[14, 15] and other mammals.[16, 17] Studies in the lower vertebrates,[18-22] especially amphibia, have influenced conceptions of behavioral development in mammals to a very considerable extent. A complete review of all articles on the subject of early fetal movements would require far more space than is available in the present chapter.

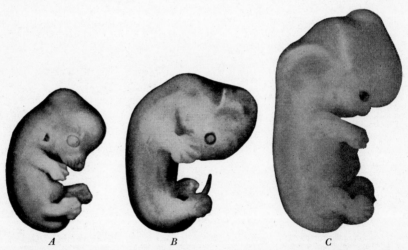

A	*B*	*C*

Fig. 47.—Embryos of the (*A*) rat, (*B*) cat and (*C*) human at approximately the stage in development at which simple reflexes are expected for the first time. Crown-rump length: 12 mm. rat; 14 mm. cat; 18 mm. human (7 weeks). Magnification: × 3.

It is impossible to say precisely when nerve cells attain the ability to discharge or when fibers can conduct nervous impulses for the first time. However, muscle contractions induced by nervous activity can be elicited surprisingly early in prenatal life. The stage at which nervous function is first observable in mammals varies to some extent, but in all species that have been investigated it is before body form has taken on the characteristic appearance of the species. In other words, somatic movements start before the close of the embryonic, rather than in the fetal period. This is illustrated by the accompanying photographs of rat, cat and human embryos taken at about the time simple reflexes can first be induced (Fig. 47).

The initiation of function in skeletal muscle cells was considered in the preceding chapter. Myogenic responses precede reflexes by at least one day in most mammals. The development of muscle fibers and of motor nerves with simple epilemmal motor nerve endings goes hand in hand, but there does not seem to be an immediate correlation between the appearance of motor endings and functional reflexes as some have suggested.[23] From the structural point of view it is possible that muscle contractions can be induced by discharge of motor neurons before reflex arcs have been completely formed. With the advent of conduction from afferent to efferent neurons through synaptic centers, reflex responses to stimulation are manifested. At this point in development behavior may be said to have its genesis.

MYOGENIC RESPONSES

Let us examine the antecedents of behavioral genesis in somewhat greater detail. Spontaneous muscle twitching characterizes embryos of certain lower vertebrates before reflex excitation becomes effective. Observations in fishes are especially notable.[19] The similarity to spontaneous contractions of myoblasts and muscle fibers in cultures of embryonic chick tissues is striking. It is possible that some of the earliest spontaneous movements observed in the intact living chick embryo[16, 21, 24, 25] are of this nature.

No comparable phenomenon has been seen in mammalian embryos studied under normal physiologic conditions. However, the movements which manifest themselves in ionically unbalanced saline solutions probably are myogenic responses.[26] Why spontaneous muscle twitching is not encountered normally in mammalian embryos has not been determined. Musculature is laid down well in advance of the time it can be activated reflexly in the rat, guinea pig, sheep and cat.

Mechanical and electrical stimuli applied directly to muscle

masses of intact embryos effect contractions readily. Micro-electrodes constructed of fine nichrome wires insulated except at the
tips serve admirably for delivering localized faradic shocks. Contractions of the embryonic skeletal muscles induced in this manner possess certain characteristics which distinguish them from
other types of somatic movement. They are as follows: (a) a
minimal stimulus, just adequate to produce a response, gives rise
to a quick contraction followed by a slower relaxation; (b) each
succeeding stimulation produces a similar contraction, for there
is no noticeable interval of fatigue during which the muscle is refractory; (c) the contraction is remarkably well localized in a
small region immediately around the tips of the electrodes and
consequently movements in several planes can usually be brought
about by shifting the position of the electrodes; (d) the embryonic muscle tissue retains a high degree of excitability irrespective of great changes in metabolic conditions. In fact, specimens which have been allowed to bleed until white, which have
cooled to room temperature and in which the heart has practically
stopped beating still respond to direct stimulation of the skeletal
musculature.

All the muscles of an embryo do not simultaneously reach a
state of development in which contractions are possible. The
first in which such direct responses can be observed are those of
the forelimbs at the attachment to the body. With advancement
of growth, excitability spreads both rostrally and caudally as well
as distally from these points.

NEUROMOTOR RESPONSES

The second step in development of behavior is thought to be
the appearance of muscle contraction in response to excitation of
motor neurons.[27] Nerve endings of a primitive kind (Fig. 45)
are present upon developing muscle fibers at a time when the
only somatic movements are those which follow direct stimulation
of the muscles.[28, 29] Although it has been impossible to obtain
direct evidence in the youngest cat embryos that purely neuromuscular contractions precede reflexes, such contractions can be
demonstrated in specimens a little more advanced, in which reflex
responses are already obtainable. After the reflexes have died
away with deterioration of the physiologic conditions of the

embryo, stimulation of motor centers produces movements. A slender and sharp dental broach was used to pierce the tissues of the back and the spinal cord of the embryos. It was found that a backward movement of the forelimb followed when the instrument was passed into the spinal cord at the level between C.7 and T.1 and a forward movement resulted in the same specimens when it was inserted at the level between C.4 and C.6. The true reflexes which had been obtained previously were all backward and outward movements of the limbs. Thus it is apparent that a new forward movement of the arm had been induced by direct stimulation of a motor center before such a movement occurred as the result of reflex stimulation of afferent nerves. It is especially noteworthy that the responses were localized and that there was no diffuse spreading of excitation through the center even with this rather crude form of stimulation. The segmental, nonintegrated character of the motor cell column of the embryonic spinal cord, so clearly evident in silver-stained histologic preparations, is demonstrable by physiologic methods.

GENESIS OF REFLEX BEHAVIOR

The third step in behavioral development is characterized by the appearance of reflexes. These do not manifest themselves until afferent and efferent neurons, simple nerve endings in peripheral tissues, connector neurons in the central nervous system and functional synaptic central mechanisms have been formed.

There are essentially two conceptions of the development of behavior in mammalian embryos. One group of investigators[2, 15, 18] believe that they have demonstrated the genesis of reflexes by a process of individuation from a fully integrated mass reaction or "total pattern." In other words, they believe that more or less discrete movements are not the primary units of behavior but that local reflexes differentiate from a more fundamental background of massive movement. Another group of investigators[10, 30] hold the opposing view that the basic elements in the genesis of mammalian behavior are relatively simple reflex responses. They find that the more complex reactions of older fetuses are formed by progressive neuronal integration of the less complicated activities of the embryo. Some other investigators[8] maintain that both theories are partially true, but are inclined to favor the former.

THE CONCEPT OF A TOTAL PATTERN

The doctrine of development of behavior from a total pattern is based on a long series of correlated physiologic and histologic studies by Coghill in the urodele amphibian, Amblystoma, appearing frequently since 1913 and summarized in his London lec-

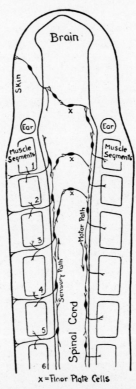

x = Floor Plate Cells

Fig. 48.—Diagram of the sensory-motor mechanism of the salamander embryo which accounts for the cephalo-caudal progression of movement away from the side stimulated. Arrows indicate direction of conduction. (Coghill: "Anatomy and the Problem of Behavior," Cambridge Univ. Press.)

tures.[18] It was found that a motor mechanism develops on either side of the embryonic floor plate as a longitudinally conducting system of neurons. Each neuron extends a process caudally to the next one; from this process branches run to the muscles of the back and later to the limbs. The series of neurons constitutes an integrating motor system which is laid down before function appears. An integrating sensory system is formed by temporary neurons, the Rohon-Beard cells in the dorsal portion of the spinal cord. They too send out processes, but in a rostral direction, with branches running to the epithelium and the muscles. The motor and sensory systems become connected by commissural floor-plate

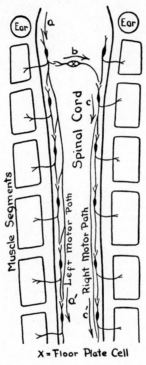

Fig. 49.—Diagram of the neuromotor mechanism of the salamander embryo which allows an initial impulse (a, a') to be followed by a contralateral secondary impulse (c, c') through an intermediate connecting neuron (b). This makes possible the swimming movements like those in Fig. 52. (Coghill: "Anatomy and the Problem of Behavior," Cambridge Univ. Press.)

neurons, appearing first near the rostral end of the embryo. These relations are illustrated in Figs. 48 and 49.

A stimulus which is applied to one side of the embryonic salamander sets up impulses which are conducted rostrally in the sensory system, across the floor-plate neurons near its rostral end, and then caudally in the integrating motor system. Contralateral flexion is thereupon the first true behavioral response; it is a mass movement or fully integrated response from the very start. This reaction is illustrated in a series of drawings taken from a motion-picture record (Fig. 50). The single flexion stage is followed shortly by bilateral flexion and then by typical swimming. The latter depends upon the appearance of collateral branches of motor neurons (Fig. 49) which allow the caudally flowing impulses of one side to precede those of the

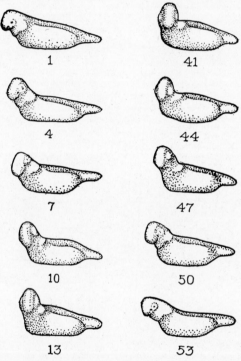

Fig. 50.—Serial tracings from motion pictures (frame numbers indicated) of the earliest contralateral movement in response to stimulation of a salamander embryo. The neural mechanism involved is illustrated in Fig. 48. (Coghill: "Anatomy and the Problem of Behavior," Cambridge Univ. Press.)

other. In this way two waves of movement can course down the trunk as shown in Figs. 51 and 52. One response coming upon another in this manner produces forward propulsion of the embryo, establishing aquatic locomotion.

Later, as the limbs grow out they first move with the trunk passively but ultimately acquire independence. Limb movements may thus be said to individuate from the mass movement

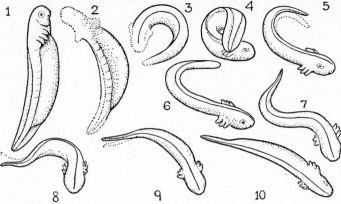

Fig. 51.—Serial tracings from motion pictures of the early swimming stage of a salamander embryo. Resting position in 1 and 10. (Coghill: "Anatomy and the Problem of Behavior," Cambridge Univ. Press.)

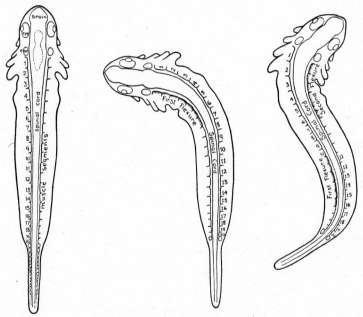

Fig. 52.—Three diagrams to show the development of the first and subsequent waves of contraction which result in swimming in the salamander embryo. (Coghill: "Anatomy and the Problem of Behavior," Cambridge Univ. Press.)

of the trunk. Terrestrial locomotion, the feeding reaction and other activities are made possible by breaking up of the original total pattern or by the formation of secondary patterns within

it.   Other more discrete reflexes individuate from these patterns
as development proceeds.   An independent and integrated motor
system is present in fishes for some time before it is captured by
developing sensory mechanisms.   During this period of independence the motor system can respond to changes in the internal
but not the external environment.[19]

In 1929 Coghill[31] attempted to explain behavior in human
embryos studied by Minkowski[32] and others in terms of the total
pattern of the salamander.   He concluded that behavior in man
follows a developmental plan of a similar type.   Some of the
earlier systematic studies on development of fetal movements in
other mammals[2, 9] suggested very strongly that nearly all embryonic motility develops from mass reactions resembling total
patterns.   The more recent interpretations of these observations
will be discussed in the latter part of the present chapter.

Human and other mammalian embryos are so very different
from Amblystoma at the time movements and reflexes first appear
that it is surprising to find any functional similarities.   The larval
salamander develops its total reaction and precisely integrated
side to side waves of movement within this integrated pattern
before limbs and mouth have been formed.   Mammalian embryos
are far from having attained functional age at a comparable stage
in morphologic differentiation (compare Figs. 47 and 50).
Muscle is entirely lacking.   Within the embryonic central nervous
system of mammals no structures exist which are comparable
with the chains of transient afferent Rohon-Beard cells of lower
forms.   Furthermore, the motor neurons are arranged segmentally
rather than in longitudinal series and they do not appear to be
connected with one another.   The earliest secondary neurons
of the spinal cord build tracts that are predominantly ascending
pathways.   In the brain, the descending tracts send few fibers into
the spinal cord until spinal behavioral responses have become
established.[33-36] *   In other words, there is no longitudinally integrating mechanism in the spinal cord of mammalian embryos at
the stage in development which corresponds to the early motile

* Recently Angulo[37] has reported that the medial longitudinal fascicle of the
spinal cord is the descending integrating tract for the mass reaction of the rat
embryo and that its termination forms the ventral spinal commissure.   This is at
variance with our own observations which show that the ventral commissure fibers
arise in the spinal cord and ascend in the ventral funiculus.

Amblystoma; nor is there until some time later. By the time differentiation of structure makes functional activities possible the head and limbs have become prominent structures.

In the further course of development of mammalian embryos these parts exert an ever increasing dominance over the trunk, and growth in the nervous system responds to this dominance. There is never a need for the type of aquatic locomotor total pattern which is found in the fishes and amphibians.

EARLY REFLEXES IN MAMMALIAN EMBRYOS

True behavior makes its appearance about one day after it was first possible to elicit muscle contractions in embryos of the rat, guinea pig, cat and sheep. It is essential to employ experimental methods which do not impair the physiologic conditions of pregnant animals and their embryos to observe the first reflexes. Furthermore, studies must be conducted immediately upon opening the uterus because this operation invariably interferes with placental respiratory exchange, resulting in anoxemia. The procedures used in such studies have been discussed in the first chapter.

Although the description of early reflex responses which follows pertains primarily to cat embryos about 14 mm. crown-rump length,[11] similar results have been obtained in other mammals.[3, 4, 6, 7] When an embryo with placenta still attached to the uterine wall has been brought quickly into view and the intact amniotic sac is percussed with some blunt instrument, pressure transmitted to the embryo through the amniotic fluid results in quick outward and backward movement of the forelimb. The movement may be called a twitch or jerk. Similar responses are obtainable in other ways. Flipping the limb gently with a needle or a hair passed through the amnion serves equally well. In a few instances it was even possible to elicit this reaction by lightly touching certain points upon the forelimb. Furthermore, faradic shocks applied to approximately the same points by means of micro-electrodes gave rise to similar quick outward and backward movements of the limb.

Another reaction is frequently elicitable in embryos 14 mm. long. Stimulation of the forward end of the head, especially the snout, results in extension of the head. When the stimulus is

applied to one side of the midline the head moves toward the opposite side and backward. When the tip of the snout is stimulated
it moves backward. Because this head response is more resistant
to changing physiologic conditions than that of the forelimb it
usually persists a little longer. Under the best conditions it too
is a quick movement. It has been observed by all investigators,
although some have encountered it at an earlier stage than others.

The head and forelimb responses are entirely separate and
distinct from one another when they first appear. They differ
somewhat in respect to the types of stimulation eliciting them but
both seem to require stronger stimuli at first than they do at a
slightly later stage in development. The head movements, being
contralateral and involving muscles some little distance away
from the site of stimulation, are certainly reflexes. All observers
agree on this point. However, some have doubted the reflex nature of the forelimb reactions, holding that they may be due to
stimulation of the muscles directly. The evidence, which will be
reviewed briefly, favors the view that they too are simple spinal-
type reflexes.

Although the limb muscles can be induced to contract by
direct stimulation in asphyxiated embryos, the response held to be
a reflex is (a) elicitable for only a brief interval (often only a
few seconds) while metabolic conditions of the embryo are at
their best. States of anoxemia set up experimentally make it impossible to obtain the reactions. After adequate direct stimulation the new muscle tends to relax slowly, whereas the reflex-like
response (b) seems to be a quicker movement with more rapid relaxation. Embryonic muscle appears to respond instantaneously
to directly applied stimuli, but (c) there is an interval just per-
ceptible between stimulus and response of the reflex type. One
muscle contraction after another can be induced by direct stimulation, but (d) a second reflex-like reaction cannot be made to follow the first one until a brief interval of time, a refractory or
fatigue period, has elapsed. Finally, (e) the responses believed to
be reflexes are stereotyped and do not show the molding characterizing direct contractions when the position of the stimulus is
varied.

Other experimental evidence demonstrates that the forelimb
movements are reflexes. When micro-electrodes are used to stim-

ulate an embryo over the spinal cord some distance caudal to the forelimb, the same quick outward and backward twitch results. This is due to conduction up the spinal cord; stimulation of other parts of the embryo, equally distant from the limbs, does not produce this movement. At least one synapse is involved as indicated in Fig. 53.

The conception of the reflex nature of the early forelimb response finds further confirmation in histologic studies in the spinal cords and peripheral nerves of the very specimens which showed the reaction and which were subsequently stained by the

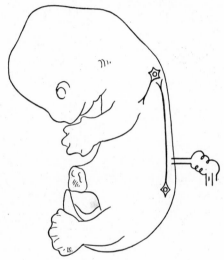

Fig. 53.—Diagram illustrating the probable nervous elements involved in eliciting forelimb movement by faradic stimulation of the spinal cord of an early mammalian embryo.

Ranson pyridine-silver technique.[28, 33–35] All nervous elements essential for reflex action are present in the embryonic spinal cord but their intrinsic synaptic connections are incomplete at the time muscles can be made to contract by stimulating them directly and previous to the appearance of the reflex-like responses. One finds afferent neurons whose peripheral fibers pass to the tissues immediately beneath the epithelium of the forelimb and whose central branches constitute the dorsal roots and dorsal funiculus of the spinal cord. The efferent neurons are assembled in two groups in the ventral gray matter of the spinal cord, a medial nucleus for trunk innervation and a lateral nucleus for the arm. The efferent axons course into the muscles of the shoulder region and end in simple terminations upon some of the muscle fibers. Commissural and associational neurons are present in the dorsal column. The former are numerous in the region just beneath the dorsomedial border of the dorsal funiculus, while the latter tend to accumulate nearer the ventrolateral border of this afferent pathway. Commissural axons pursue a course ventrally through

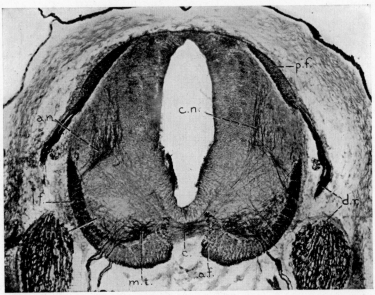

Fig. 54.—Photomicrograph of the fifth cervical segment of the spinal cord of a 13 mm. cat embryo just before the time the first forelimb reflexes can be elicited. *a.f.*, ventral funiculus; *a.n.*, association neurons; *c.*, commissure; *c.n.*, commissural neurons; *d.r.*, dorsal root and ganglion; *l.f.*, lateral funiculus; *m.l.*, motor nucleus for the limb muscles; *m.t.*, motor nucleus for the trunk muscles; *p.f.*, dorsal funiculus. Compare with Fig. 56. Pyridine-silver stain; × 80.

the gray matter and cross the floor plate, to become an ascending tract close to the motor nerve cells which supply the trunk. Associational axons pass close to the motor nucleus for limb muscles and enter the lateral funiculus. This relation of associational neurons and primary motor forelimb neurons appears to be very intimate, with axons of the former coursing parallel with dendrons of the latter. However, up to the time of appearance of the forelimb response there is no close relationship between the primary afferent and the secondary neurons (Fig. 54). A few collateral branches of dorsal funiculus fibers do pass for a very short distance toward the associational group, but not many have reached it.

In the early motile embryos in which reflex-like twitches of the forelimb occurred when the limbs were flipped or when the amniotic sac was percussed, connections have been completed between the primary afferent and the associational neurons.   This is

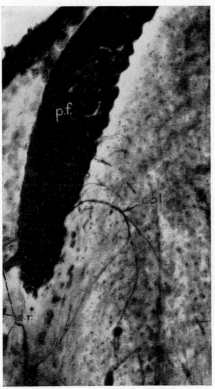

Fig. 55.—Photomicrograph of the dorsal funiculus (*p.f.*) of the spinal cord of a 13 mm. cat embryo showing the first collateral branches (*col.*) of primary afferent neurons; these serve to complete the first spinal reflex arcs. Pyridine-silver stain; × 510.

accomplished when collateral branches grow in among the cells of the dorsal gray horn from the sensory fibers nearest the lateral border of the dorsal funiculus. Some of the longest collaterals enter the nucleus of motor cells supplying the forelimb muscles. These relationships will be seen in accompanying photomicrographs (Figs. 54 and 55) and diagrams (Figs. 56 and 57). The organization of the first structural reflex mechanism is clearly such that when it begins to function the response will not only be homolateral but will be confined to the segments at which the impulses enter the spinal cord.   The greatest number and the

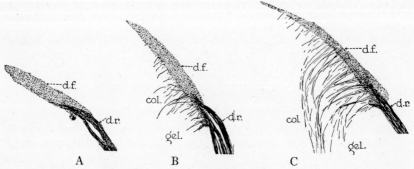

Fig. 56.—Camera lucida tracings of the dorsal roots (*d.r.*) and dorsal funiculus (*d.f.*) of sheep embryos (*A*) 20 mm., (*B*) 23 mm., and (*C*) 24 mm. long.   The development of collaterals (*col.*) of the dorsal funiculus which curve medially around the gelatinous substance (*gel.*) of the gray matter is correlated with the appearance of the first forelimb reflexes.   Pyridine-silver stain; × 72.

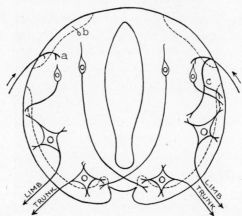

Fig. 57.—Diagrammatic cross section through the embryonic spinal cord just before (left side) and just after (right side) the completion of reflex arcs make the earliest reflexes elicitable. The earliest connections of afferent neurons (*a*) appear at the lateral end of the dorsal funiculus and complete unisegmental reflex arcs. Some of these involve an interneuron but others (*c*) make direct connections with the primary motor neurons for the limb muscles. Only later do the dorsal funiculus fibers from lower segments of the spinal cord connect with the commissural interneurons by means of collaterals (*b*) and thus effect contralateral trunk movements.

longest new collaterals first grow into the gray matter in the brachial region and, correlatively, one finds the first reflex response involving the forelimbs.

The correlation between completion of anatomical reflex arcs in the spinal cords of cat embryos and the manifestation of forelimb reflex function has been confirmed in the chick, rat and sheep. The stage of development reached in the spinal cord of these four species at the time reflexes appear varies to some extent, but the responses occur in all at the time reflex arcs are ready irrespective of other structural variations.

Such evidence as has been disclosed by the correlated histologic and physiologic experiments reviewed here briefly leads to the conclusion that the early forelimb movements are local, unisegmental, homolateral two- and three-neuron reflexes. Mammalian behavior has its genesis, not in a mass reaction or total pattern like that of lower vertebrates, but in these relatively simple reflexes which are at first entirely nonintegrated.

OTHER SIMPLE REFLEXES AND THEIR INTEGRATION

During the course of development of cat embryos, many reflexes make their appearance. Just as the first responses at the shoulder can be elicited before the limbs move spontaneously and before they move with the neck and trunk, local reflexes appear at the elbow and wrist joints as separate entities before the distal portions of the limbs become integrated with other parts of the body. Local flexion at the elbows occurs at about the 16-mm. stage. It is often followed by other more distant movements, such as bending at the shoulder or extension of the head and flexion of the trunk. However, these more proximal and cephalic movements are not followed by movement at the elbow at this time. Similarly, local wrist movements, seen in embryos about 17 mm. long, are at first unrelated to other movements.

Local movements at the proximal hind-leg joint, unintegrated with trunk responses, are encountered in specimens between 15 and 16 mm. long. Those at the knee appear at 17.5 mm. The earliest independent motility of the tail is found at the same stage.

Although the first head reflexes can be elicited by stimulating only a small area near the tip of the snout in embryos 13–14 mm. long, it is but a short time later that they occur in response to stimulation of most of the facial area. In specimens 15–16 mm. long, contralateral head flexion is obtainable from all parts of the face except that supplied by the ophthalmic division of the trigeminal nerve. From the ophthalmic region, extension with flexion to the same side occurs. With further development, stimulation of more and more portions of the face leads to the homolateral response until, at about the 20 mm. stage, only the ear gives a contralateral head flexion.

These and other interesting reflex activities have been observed in embryos. All possess an element of individuality at first, but ultimately most of the local responses are brought together into more generalized movements. This comes about by integration within the framework of a growing central nervous mechanism. Longitudinal tracts of nerve fibers develop within the spinal cord, and as they make connections with afferent and efferent neurons they begin to exert an integrating function over the local, isolated reactions.

The earliest secondary pathway in the spinal cord is a ventral longitudinal bundle, primarily an ascending tract formed by the axons of commissural neurons. Impulses carried by it apparently are able to discharge motor neurons supplying trunk and neck muscles at more rostral levels. Cell bodies of the commissural neurons, lying near the medial border of the dorsal funiculus, receive impulses from primary afferent neurons which have been coursing rostrally for some distance in the dorsal funiculus. Consequently the local homolateral forelimb reflex is sometimes followed, at the 15 to 16 mm. stage, by a contraction of neck muscles. Similarly at a later period, hind-limb reflexes are followed progressively by responses of the forelimbs and the neck. A progressive discharge of neurons from caudal to rostral regions of the spinal cord is brought about through integration of ascending neurons of the primary afferent dorsal funiculus with the commissural secondary tract.

Nerve fibers grow caudally into the spinal cord from centers in the medulla oblongata and midbrain. Many of these occupy positions in the ventral funiculus but they do not reach any given point in the spinal cord until after ascending fibers from a lower spinal segment have reached the medulla oblongata. Consequently stimulation of structures near the caudal end of an embryo of about 18 mm. (Fig. 58) can result sequentially in (a) local reflexes, (b) reflexes of more rostral parts, (c) head movements and then (d) the trunk activities which are integrated with the head and which always fall just short of the most recently acquired local responses. The descending integrating tracts of nerve fibers are so placed in the ventral portion of the spinal cord that when activated they can more effectively bring about discharge of motor cells which supply the trunk muscles than neurons for the limb muscles. As a result of such an arrangement the limbs seem not to be completely integrated with the trunk during the early embryonic period. Later the association becomes more intimate. On the other hand, the trunk movements become integrated with those of the neck almost as soon as they

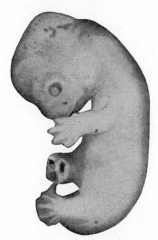

Fig. 58.—Cat embryo 18.5 mm. C. R. length, from which local reflexes as well as early integrated movements could be elicited. Magnification is the same as that in Figs. 44 and 47.

begin to appear at the 15 mm. stage. With growth in size of the individual, more and more muscles of the back are added to the trunk activities in a caudally expanding progression.

Some recent experiments involving the production of states of anoxemia[12] have added important information to our conception of the relation of simple reflexes to the more massive integrated activities of cat embryos. When decerebrate cats were allowed to breathe atmospheres low in oxygen before the uterus was opened it was found that local reflexes became depressed and the integrated head and trunk movements were exaggerated and more sustained or tonic than normally. Irritability of the embryos was diminished during anoxemia. Extended use of the gas mixture brought about more complete anoxemia and all responses ceased. Spontaneous movements and responses to stimulation of embryos studied under conditions of partial anoxemia resemble mass reactions and might easily lead one to the conclusion that behavior develops in mammals in a manner very similar to that in the salamander. Only when such conditions are avoided can the various simple reflexes be observed as separate elements.

REFERENCES CITED

1. Swenson, E. A. 1926. Thesis, Univ. Kansas.
2. Angulo y Gonzalez, A. W. 1932. J. Comp. Neur., 55: 395.
3. Raney, E. T. & L. Carmichael. 1934. J. Genetic Psychol., 45: 3.
4. Windle, W. F., W. L. Minear, M. F. Austin & D. W. Orr. 1935. Physiol. Zool., 8: 156.
5. Carmichael, L. 1934. Genetic Psychol. Mono., 16: 337.
6. Bridgman, C. S. & L. Carmichael. 1935. J. Genetic Psychol., 47: 247.
7. Barcroft, J., D. H. Barron & W. F. Windle. 1936. J. Physiol., 87: 73.
8. Barcroft, J. & D. H. Barron. 1939. J. Comp. Neur., 70: 477.
9. Windle, W. F. & A. M. Griffin. 1931. J. Comp. Neur., 52: 149.
10. Windle, W. F., J. E. O'Donnell & E. E. Glasshagle. 1933. Physiol. Zool., 6: 521.
11. Windle, W. F., D. W. Orr & W. L. Minear. 1934. Physiol. Zool., 7: 600.
12. Windle, W. F. & R. F. Becker. 1940. Arch. Neur. Psychiat., 43: 90.
13. Coronios, J. D. 1933. Genetic Psychol. Mono., 14: 283.
14. Minkowski, M. 1938. Abderhalden's Handb. biol. Arbeitsmeth, Abt. V, Teil 5B: 511.
15. Hooker, D. 1936. Yale J. Biol. Med., 8: 579.
16. Preyer, W. 1885. Specielle Physiologie des Embryo. Grieben, Leipzig.
17. Pankratz, D. S. 1931. Anat. Rec., 49: 31.
18. Coghill, G. E. 1929. Anatomy and the Problem of Behavior. Macmillan, New York.
19. Tracy, H. C. 1926. J. Comp. Neur., 40: 253.
20. Tuge, H. 1931. Proc. Soc. Exp. Biol. & Med., 29: 52.
21. Kuo, Z. Y. 1932. J. Exper. Zool., 61: 395.
22. Youngstrom, K. A. 1938. J. Comp. Neur., 68: 351.
23. East, E. W. 1931. Anat. Rec., 50: 201.
24. Clark, E. L. & E. R. Clark. 1914. J. Exp. Zool., 17: 373.
25. Orr, D. W. & W. F. Windle. 1934. J. Comp. Neur., 60: 271.
26. Windle, W. F. 1939. Physiol. Zool., 12: 39.
27. Angulo y Gonzalez, A. W. 1933. Proc. Soc. Exp. Biol. & Med., 31: 111.
28. Windle, W. F. 1937. Ibid., 36: 640.
29. Scharpenberg, L. G. & W. F. Windle. 1938. J. Anat., 72: 344.
30. Carmichael, L. 1933. In C. Murchison's Handb. Child Psychol., 2nd ed., Chap. 2, p. 31, Clark Univ. Press, Worcester, Mass.
31. Coghill, G. E. 1929. Arch. Neur. & Psychiat., 21: 989.

32. Minkowski, M. 1922. Schweiz. med. Wochenschr., 52: 721, 751.
33. Windle, W. F. 1934. J. Comp. Neur., 59: 487.
34. Windle, W. F. & D. W. Orr. 1934. Ibid., 60: 287.
35. Windle, W. F. & R. E. Baxter. 1936. Ibid., 63: 189.
36. Windle, W. F. & J. E. Fitzgerald. 1937. Ibid., 67: 493.
37. Angulo y Gonzalez, A. W. 1939. Ibid., 71: 325.

CHAPTER XI

CONDITIONS REGULATING FETAL NERVOUS ACTIVITY

THERE is no doubt that the progressive development of nervous function is related to differentiation of structure in the fetal nervous system. It was hoped that many correlations like those discussed in Chapter X could be drawn between specific responses and the appearance histologically of new neural connections. This is not an easy task because structural growth proceeds with great rapidity and results in the establishment very early of complexities defying microscopic analysis. On the other hand, function in the central nervous system of the fetus is not regulated solely by structural factors. One must not lose sight of metabolic influences; it is quite clear that variations in fetal activities are closely related to changing respiratory conditions. The parts played by the blood, the heart and vascular system and even the endocrine glands have to be determined. Many problems in physiology of the fetal nervous system await solution, but it will be well to view some of them, even though questions raised thereby can not be given satisfactory answers.

THE PLAN OF STRUCTURAL DEVELOPMENT OF THE FETAL BRAIN

Knowledge of development of intrinsic brain structure is far from complete, for it has been within the past few years only that systematic studies in specimens prepared by adequate methods were undertaken. The usual histologic procedures are unsatisfactory to demonstrate embryonic nerve fibers, their terminations and relations to one another inside the brain and spinal cord. Cajal's silver stains, especially the Ranson modification, bring out details of this nature incomparably better than any other known technique.[1] Procedures of this type are being used extensively for studying the prenatal mammalian nervous system in this[2-12] and the Madrid[13-17] laboratories, as well as in a few other places.[18-22]

By the time fetal movements can be elicited for the first time in any species, a surprisingly extensive organization of neuron groups

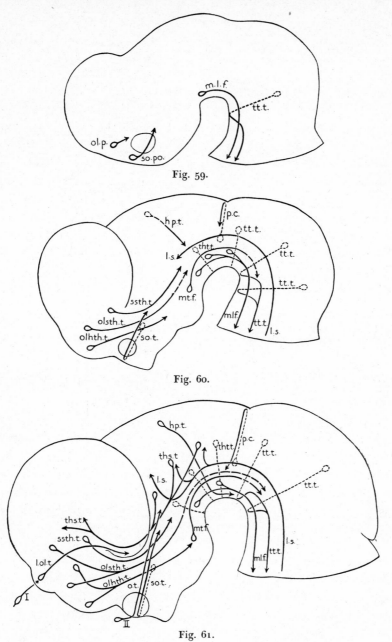

Fig. 59.

Fig. 60.

Fig. 61.

Figs. 59–61.—Diagrams of the brains of cat embryos 7 mm. (Fig. 59) , 10 mm. (Fig. 60) and 15 mm. (Fig. 61) C. R. length showing the principal fiber tracts present in each. Crossing neurons are dotted lines. Questionable courses: dash lines.

and fiber tracts has already formed within the central nervous system. We have discussed certain correlations between intrinsic spinal connections and the first forelimb reflexes. In the brain equally specific correlations have not been worked out completely. Most of the tracts and nuclei have been identified in cat embryos and those that are present at the time behavior has its genesis are

TABLE 21

CLASSIFICATION OF NERVE FIBERS OF THE TELENCEPHALON AND DIENCEPHALON OF 15-MM. CAT EMBRYOS ACCORDING TO APPROXIMATE ORDER OF APPEARANCE

Name of fiber group	Abbreviations used in figs. 59–61	Size of smallest embryo in which it was found
		mm.
Medial longitudinal fascicle.................	m. l. f.	5.5
Supraoptic system: direct preoptic component.	so. po.	6.0
Supraoptic system: commissural component...	so. t.	7.0
Olfacto-hypothalamic fibers.................	olhth. t.	7.0
Olfacto-subthalamic fibers..................	olsth. t.	8.0
Strio-subthalamic fibers....................	ssth. t.	8.0
Direct subthalamo-tegmental fibers (diffuse)..		8.0
Crossed pretecto-tegmental and thalamo-tegmental fibers (ventral commissure)......	th. t.; tht. t.	8.0
Lemniscus system.........................	l. s.	8.0
Terminal nerve fibers......................		10.0
Posterior commissure fibers.................	p. c.	10.0
Habenulo-peduncular fibers.................	hp. t.	10.0
Lateral olfactory tract fibers................	l. ol. t.	11.5
Mammillo-tegmental tract fibers.............	mt. f.	11.5
Optic nerve fibers.........................	II	11.5
Thalamo-strial and thalamo-cortical fibers.....	ths. t.	11.5
Mammillo-thalamic fibers...................		13.5
Olfactory nerve fibers......................	I	13.0

listed in Table 21. Figs. 59 to 61 illustrate diagrammatically and incompletely this extensive development of tracts in the rostral portions of the embryonic brain.

(a) ORDER OF DEVELOPMENT IN FUNCTIONAL SYSTEMS

Within the growing tangle of nerve fibers it is possible to distinguish several systems of functionally related tracts. They appear to be growing in anticipation of the time they will conduct impulses to distant effector organs. Such systems of tracts are laid down economically; for the most part they pursue the shortest possible courses from place to place. One of the most interesting features of growth of each system is the order in which its component tracts are formed. This is from motor toward sensory side.

The very first neurons which can be recognized in the embryo are primary motor elements of the spinal and cranial nerves, present in rat embryos only 3 mm. long and appearing in the other species at comparable stages. These are final common path neurons over which impulses must ultimately pass to bring about responses in the muscles of the body. They are the first, local connecting neurons are second and the primary afferent tracts appear third.

The earliest secondary connecting neurons make their appearance in 17 day old cat embryos in the portion of the medulla oblongata which will become the reticular formation. Growth very soon spreads into the upper spinal cord segments. There, nerve cells give rise to crossed and direct axons which make local connections with primary motor elements. Some in the medulla oblongata form the earliest reticulospinal fibers, but they do not extend their processes far along the nerve axis. Secondary elements of the spinal cord enter into the formation of local conduction systems, all components of which are not present however until primary afferent neurons begin to build the sensory tracts. Even then, the local systems do not become functional reflex mechanisms until synaptic relations between the three elements—motor, connector and sensory—have been established on the 24th day in the cat embryos. Similar reflex arcs are completed during the 8th week in man.

Almost simultaneously with the appearance of secondary neurons in the medulla oblongata, another group begins to be laid down in front of the mesencephalon. Fibers from this source descend to the lower part of the brain stem without crossing and form one component of the medial longitudinal fascicle. It seems probable that the early secondary neurons are related to more than one basic reflex system. Just as the lower motor neurons are not an exclusive component of any one system, so these interneurons may be shared by several.

Secondary neurons make their appearance in still another location in the early embryo. Crossing and direct fibers arise in the mesencephalic tectum and form the tectobulbar and tectospinal tracts. Thus we find essentially four groups of secondary neurons undergoing development in the central nervous system between the 18th and 20th days of gestation in the cat and during the 5th week in man. These are (a) local intrasegmental and intersegmental elements, such as later constitute the ground bundles of the spinal cord, (b) reticulospinal tracts, (c) medial longitudinal fascicles and (d) tectobulbar and tectospinal tracts. Few fibers course farther caudally than the lower end of the medulla oblongata until a day or so after initiation of the first individual head and forelimb reflexes. However, it can not be doubted that one or more of these tracts play a part in the earliest cephalocaudal integration of movements which occurs on the 25th day in cat embryos.

Secondary neurons of the spinal cord, especially commissural, course rostrally in the ventral and lateral funiculi. These are present before a significant number of descending fibers from the brain reach the cord. They account for conduction of impulses from caudal to rostral segments and explain the observation of forelimb and head reflexes which sometimes follow stimulation of more caudal structures.

(b) GROWTH OF OTHER CIRCUITS FOR REFLEXES AND HIGHER INTEGRATION

Just as the intrasegmental neurons of the spinal cord enter into the structure of basic short reflex circuits, reticulospinal, tectospinal and medial longitudinal fibers constitute links in longer circuits which become functional much later than the local ones. Examples of such systems are the olfactory and optic reflex mechanisms of the early embryo. Analysis of the growth of these systems shows that their component tracts too are laid down from efferent to afferent side. For example, during development of the optic-reflex conduction mechanism the primary spinal motor and the oculomotor neurons begin to form first, secondary neurons represented by the medial longitudinal and tectospinal tracts are next, the posterior commissure follows, the optic tract itself is fourth, and finally the retinal bipolar neurons and visual cells appear. Similar sequential development seems to be the rule in other reflex conduction systems.

Within any conduction system such as the optic or olfactory, the simplest reflex pathways are formed before those which have to do with perception and higher integrative activities. Neuro-fibrillar development is late in the cerebellum, corpus striatum and cerebral cortex. A primitive secondary afferent tract, medial lemniscus in part, reaches the thalamus of cat embryos from spinal and bulbar centers by the 21st day of gestation. Fibers begin to pass from the thalamus to the cerebrum on the 22nd day, but not until late in fetal life does the cerebral cortex exert any influence over lower motor parts of the nervous system. The pyramidal tracts are last to form.

Correlated with the tardy development of cerebral cortex, it has been determined that cerebral electric potentials are absent throughout most of prenatal life. Even in the guinea pig, an animal which is much more mature than the rat, cat or man at the time of birth, they do not manifest themselves until about 2 or 3 weeks before the end of the gestation period.[23] A cortical control of the motor mechanism for forelimbs has been established at the time of birth in the cat, but the hind limbs lack it until 16 days later.[24]

(c) MYELOGENY AS RELATED TO FUNCTION IN THE NERVOUS SYSTEM

Many neurologists adhere to the theory that the initiation and maturation of function of the nervous system depends upon the formation of myelin sheaths. Flechsig[25] called attention to the fact that the progress of deposition of myelin is orderly and that tracts having definite functions become myelinated at different times in the human infant's brain. Some investigators[26] who have studied the course of development of behavior in kittens and have attempted to correlate it with myelin formation have suggested functional relationships. Others[24, 27-31] have carried out similar studies in pouch-young opossum, kitten and human infant brains as well as in the fetal nervous system of the cat and man. In a general way it seemed that maturation of behavior and the acquisition of myelin sheaths of certain fiber tracts were related, but it was impossible to draw specific correlations in all cases. For example, the corticospinal tract is still unmyelinated at birth but cortical areas for control of forelimbs are electrically excitable.

There can be a great deal of well organized activity in the brain before any nerve fibers become myelinated.[32] In the cat, myelin is present neither in the peripheral nerve roots nor in the tracts of the spinal cord and brain before the 42nd day of fetal life.[33]   But 30 day old cat fetuses can execute rhythmical respiratory and other coordinated reflex movements similar to those employing myelinated tracts at a later time.   The early behavioral reactions of the rat are certainly executed in the absence of myelinated nerve fibers.[32, 34]

An attempt was made to correlate specific righting reflexes of cat fetuses with development of myelin sheaths on the nerve fibers which were involved.[33]   It was demonstrated that the vestibular righting reaction appears coincidentally with sheaths upon the fibers of the vestibular nerve and that conduction pathways used in the reaction are partially myelinated when the reflex first occurs.   However, the righting response to sensory impulses from the skin and deep tissues of the body, i. e., a body righting reflex, is manifested before that employing the labyrinthine apparatus. Its neural mechanism is incompletely myelinated at the time.

It is possible that myelination is more closely related to the order of development of tracts in the embryonic nervous system than to specific functional activities.   Thus we find parts of the medial longitudinal and reticulospinal systems of neurons appearing early and receiving their myelin sheaths first.   But the correlation is not absolute and many discrepancies can be observed.   About all that one can say is that the first tracts to develop in the embryo are the first to begin to be myelinated and the last to form in the late fetus are the last to receive sheaths. Some tracts never develop significant numbers of myelin sheaths. It is quite probable that conduction of impulses may be improved with the acquisition of myelin, but myelination is certainly not an essential corollary of function.   With increasing fetal size, distances between points in the nervous system become greater. Perhaps myelin is laid down to compensate by increasing the conduction speed of the fibers.

FACTORS OTHER THAN STRUCTURAL GROWTH
(a) THE QUIESCENCE OF INTRA-UTERINE LIFE

It is relatively easy to elicit nervous activities throughout the greater part of prenatal life in the guinea pig, cat, sheep and man under certain experimental conditions.   But it should not be assumed that all responses which can be induced occur spontaneeously within the uterus of the normal intact individual. As a matter of fact, there is scanty evidence that any of them occur normally during the early part of the gestation period.

Human fetal movements can be detected as early as the 14th week by means of a stethoscope, but the mother is usually unable to feel them before the 17th week of gestation. It is difficult to diagnose them accurately much before the latter time without considerable experience, for they are often confused with the sounds produced by movements of intestinal gases. Fetuses of experimental animals appear to be singularly quiet until late in prenatal life when occasional quick jerks or twitches can be observed upon the maternal abdomen. Surprisingly little fetal activity is seen even when the thin-walled uterus is delivered under local anesthesia.

Although the few fetal movements which are readily visible in the intact individual seem to be purposeless, we know that some well coordinated and useful activities do take place normally during the second half of prenatal life. For example, intrauterine swallowing has been proved to be a normal physiologic function.[35] This is an activity engaged in with great regularity during the last third of gestation in the guinea pig. We do not know its cause (see Chapter VII).

(b) AFFERENT STIMULATION IN UTERO

The relative quiescence of the normal fetus in utero is somewhat surprising when one considers all the activities of which the growing specimen is capable when removed from the uterus. The reason seems to be at least twofold: lack of adequate stimulation and high thresholds in the fetal central nervous system. The fetus is adequately nourished and warmed in a medium lacking practically all the stimulating influences of the environment with which it will have to cope later on. No significant excitation of the external receptors occurs.

Experimental evidence in the cat supports the view that there is little spontaneous motor discharge in the absence of afferent impulses. In several hundred embryos and young fetuses delivered under good physiologic conditions and without using anesthesia, spontaneous movements have rarely been seen at the moment of delivery. They make their appearance within a few seconds or minutes, apparently because placental exchange has been jeopardized or because changes in the environment cause stimulation. One can not avoid manipulation entirely, and even though every effort is made to maintain the placental circulation intact, incision of the uterus disturbs the relationship between uterus and placenta. The resulting anoxemia accounts partially for the movements.

If there were a true automaticity of embryonic motor neurons, spontaneous movements should be observed in many instances at the moment the specimens are brought into view. But there is very little motor discharge without afferent stimulation. Rhythmical movements have been seen in sheep embryos 40 to 50 days old at the moment of delivery and it has been suggested that the responses are automatic.[36] Some are definitely initiated by mechanical stimulation in the younger embryos. It was proposed that the automatic movements of the sheep fetus become inhibited as soon as descending secondary tracts grow down into the spinal cord from the brain stem. In the cat, no rhythmical movements can be obtained until *after* tracts have grown down; responses between 23 and 28 days of gestation are neither automatic nor rhythmic.

(c) NEURAL THRESHOLDS TO STIMULATION

Later in prenatal life all fetuses become less responsive to stimulation than they were at first. How much this may be due to inhibition over newly developed descending pathways from the brain we do not know. Guinea pig and cat fetuses near term do not respond actively to ordinary manual palpation through the intact abdomen but they can be aroused from their profound "slumber" by pricking or prodding them with a needle thrust into the abdomen and uterus. It seems reasonable to conclude that the fetal nervous system has developed high thresholds. At any rate, fetal motor centers are less excitable than they were earlier in prenatal life and less excitable than those of newborn individuals.

But the excitability of fetuses in utero can be enhanced experimentally. One way to do so is to reduce the oxygen available in the fetal brain without creating complete asphyxia. Partial anoxemia at all times in prenatal life predisposes toward an increase in fetal movements, but most activities are not actually induced through the internal environment by chemical stimuli.

They follow mechanical stimuli which were subliminal before the anoxemia was set up. This was demonstrated in experiments like the following one.

At 63 days of gestation, fetuses of a decerebrated cat were observed to be very quiet in utero. When a needle was passed through the abdominal wall and into the uterus, the fetuses responded to prodding; they executed brief kicks on non-respiratory jerks of the head which stopped almost immediately after stimulation ceased. With the needle still in place, the cat was allowed to rebreathe air in a rubber tube with wide bore. Stimulation of the fetuses was repeated; this time the responses were much

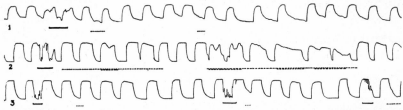

Fig. 62.—Three portions of a crystograph record showing maternal respirations (large waves, 16 per minute) broken up by intrauterine fetal movements. The cat (63 days gestation) had been decerebrated by the anemia method; no anesthesia was used during the experiment; the abdomen was not opened but a long needle had been passed through the abdominal wall into one amniotic sac. At the heavy solid lines, the fetus was stimulated with the needle and the irregular deflections on the record at these points are due to this mechanical effect. Fetal movements were observed at the points indicated by the broken lines; these movements were slight in records 1 and 3, during which the cat was breathing air. In record 2, the cat was rebreathing to induce a partial anoxemia; stimulation led to marked prolonged fetal movements of a tonic squirming type (double broken lines) which caused considerable interference in the maternal respiratory record.

more active, the fetuses kicked and squirmed for some time after the cessation of the stimulus and the movements were tonic and sustained. The rebreathing tube was then removed and as soon as the mother's breathing had become normal again the fetuses were restimulated. Results were obtained like those before the anoxemia. One experiment of this type is illustrated in the parts of a continuous record reproduced in Fig. 62.

Certain very rapid rhythmical movements of respiratory muscles do appear to be elicited by endogenous chemical stimulation of the fetal respiratory center.[37] They can be induced by raising the carbon dioxide level in the blood during the early part of active fetal life, but can not be called forth by this method in the late fetal period unless a rather marked oxygen deficiency is brought on too.   These observations suggest a rising threshold in the fetal nervous system of the cat with advancing prenatal age.

Respiratory rhythms are quite independent of most other somatic movements in the cat. At the time they are first obtainable, they involve only the muscles which are normally used by the adult for breathing, *i. e.*, the diaphragm, intercostals and abdominals. A little later in fetal life, they can be made to involve neck and trunk muscles if the degree of anoxemia used to elicit them is increased. Respiratory rhythms often set off other somatic movements in cat fetuses but are themselves less frequently started by some non-respiratory twitch. Indeed, the cat fetus when stimulated in the intact uterus can be induced to kick or move its head vigorously without any movement of a respiratory nature following.

(d) Muscle Tonus and Mass Movements

Not only does anoxemia facilitate the effectiveness of subliminal mechanical stimulation and induce automatic rhythmical respiration-like movements but it also brings about changes in the character of motor responses when its severity is increased beyond the point of facilitation. Early in the gestation period of the cat, local reflexes of the limbs are abolished more readily than those of the trunk and neck under anoxemia. Throughout the middle of prenatal life, stimulation of anoxemic fetuses leads to responses which resemble mass reactions, any adequate stimulus eliciting not local movements but generalized activities such as squirming.[38]

Movements of anoxemic cat fetuses lacked the "jerky" quality they had shown beforehand and became more sustained and tonic. A single stimulus often results in repeated movements suggestive of considerable after-discharge in motor centers. Under marked anoxemia, such as that following occlusion of the umbilical cord, fetal muscles sometimes become so hypertonic that the fetus resembles a decerebrate animal. Similar postures have been observed in kittens and rabbits (see Fig. 64) decerebrated by sectioning the brain at the rostral border of the mesencephalon.[39] The increase in muscle tonus under asphyxial conditions may be interpreted as a protective mechanism. It acts to insure the expansion of the chest which is necessary for air breathing.[40]

To what extent anoxemia is normal and physiologic in pre-natal life is not known.* Observations in early stages of several species of animals suggest that it may follow experimental procedures more readily in some than in others. This may be due in part to species variation in the placenta as an organ for oxygen exchange in early fetal life. It is possible that embryos of animals like the sheep, which have rather primitive syndesmo-chorial placentas, may tolerate operative procedures involving some manipulation of the uterus less well than other forms such as the cat or guinea pig, which have their maternal and fetal blood streams in more intimate contact (see Chapter I). Theoretically, an equal amount of trauma would be more disastrous in the former than in the latter. The fact that it was more difficult to observe the very first reflexes in sheep than in cat and guinea pig embryos and that there is more of a tendency for movements, seemingly automatic, to manifest themselves in sheep than in cat embryos, would fit into such a conception.

(e) Susceptibility Gradients to Asphyxia

The exact nature of changes which depress neural thresholds under oxygen deficiency is unknown. They may be chemical or physical. Some investigators have suggested that certain fetal movements result from stimulation of the nervous system by accumulating metabolic end-products, principally carbon dioxide.[41-44] Although it is true that automatic, rhythmical, respiratory movements can be initiated by increasing the carbon dioxide content of fetal blood experimentally, those induced by asphyxiation may be related less to an increase in the chemical stimulus than to a depression of thresholds (increase of neuron excitability).

It has been postulated[45, 46] that endogenous (chemical) stimulation affects the motor centers directly and acts first on the most recently developed units, that the new neurons have the highest physiologic gradient and are consequently stimulated first by accumulating metabolites in the blood. The evidence is open to question because experimental conditions were not well controlled. The embryos were studied in unbalanced saline solutions. It has been demonstrated more recently[47] that the waving of embryonic limbs and tail, which suggested the theory, occurs

* See J. Barcroft, et al., 1940, J. Physiol., 97: 338, 347.

only in embryos placed in solutions deficient in calcium and potassium and is not necessarily related to accumulating metabolites.

Under asphyxia, the behavior of fetal sheep tends to revert to a type characterizing younger specimens but a clear cut recapitulation of development of reflex movements was not found.[36]   Simple reflexes most recently acquired apparently were not called forth during asphyxia.   In the cat[38] it has been observed that asphyxia abolishes activities in a rather orderly manner.   It has a more destructive action upon the appendicular motor mechanism than upon that of the neck and trunk.   The last activity to disappear under asphyxia is a respiratory movement of the chest.   This confirms a previous observation in bird fetuses[48]; it was found that deep rhythmical gasping could be induced repeatedly by tying and untying the allantoic vessels.   It seems probable that motor centers show gradients of susceptibility to asphyxia but there is no evidence that the oldest reflexes, *i. e.,* those of the neck and forelimb, are the last to be affected by the asphyxia.

(f) INHIBITION OF MOTOR MECHANISMS BY HIGHER CENTERS

It has been suggested that the changes in behavior of sheep fetuses under asphyxia may result from the removal of inhibitory influences of new descending nerve tracts of higher order upon lower motor neurons.[36]   This view conforms to the conception of a gradient of susceptibility to destruction by asphyxia, the new higher order neurons being thrown out of function before the older motor neurons.   It also assumes some sort of automaticity in the lower motor centers.

Transection of the fetal brain stem and spinal cord at various levels below the mesencephalon was performed in ten fetuses 50 to 76 days old without removing them from the uterus.[36]   One to 13 days later the abdomens of the ewes were opened again and the fetuses delivered by Caesarean section.   Fetal movements at that time resembled those characterizing unoperated specimens at 40 to 50 days gestation.   It was suggested that the operations had released lower motor mechanisms from inhibitory influences of nervous centers above the transection level in the region of the red nucleus.   On the other hand one investigator[49] encountered no qualitative difference in behavior of newborn rats whose cerebrum (alone or with other parts of the brain above the medulla oblongata) had been destroyed in utero and their normal litter mate controls.

It is probably true that sheep as well as other mammalian fetuses are endowed with relatively lower thresholds in early fetal life than later on toward term, and that structural growth within the brain plays an important part in determining the nature of thresholds. The theory that motor centers are held in check by the descending tracts is a very attractive one and deserves careful study, but more experiments in other species of animals must be performed before it can be proved.

Other studies have been made with results suggestive of the phenomenon in question. Minkowski[50] observed a reversal of the type of response in the human plantar reflex. During the course of its development plantar flexion preceded dorsal flexion from stimulating the sole, and after the latter had become well established it commonly changed back to plantar flexion under narcosis as well as progressive asphyxia. Others have disagreed with his interpretations,[51] and personal experience has shown that the Babinski reflex (dorsal flexion) of the human fetus is remarkably resistant to asphyxia. When it does succumb, the plantar flexion which remains appears to result from direct stimulation of the muscles in the sole of the foot.

The earliest head movements of cat embryos are contralateral. With further development they change to homolateral responses, but under asphyxia they sometimes become contralateral again. Extension of the head of the early sheep fetus usually accompanies the respiratory-like rhythms of movement, but after a time, during which a partial anoxemia builds up, extension changes to flexion.[52] These and other examples show how progressive asphyxia exerts selective action upon the central nervous system. Similar results have been observed in adult animals.[53]

REFERENCES CITED

1. Davenport, H. A., W. F. Windle & R. H. Beech. 1934. Stain Tech., 9: 5.
2. Windle, W. F. 1931. J. Comp. Neur., 53: 71.
3. Windle, W. F. 1932. Ibid., 55: 99.
4. Windle, W. F. 1932. Ibid., 55: 315.
5. Windle, W. F. 1933. Ibid., 58: 643.
6. Windle, W. F. 1934. Ibid., 59: 487.
7. Windle, W. F. 1935. Ibid., 63: 139.
8. Windle, W. F. & R. E. Baxter. 1936. Ibid., 63: 173.

9. Windle, W. F. & R. E. Baxter. 1936. Ibid., 63: 189.
10. Windle, W. F. 1937. Proc. Soc. Exper. Biol. & Med., 36: 640.
11. Windle, W. F. & J. E. Fitzgerald. 1937. J. Comp. Neur., 67: 493.
12. Scharpenberg, L. G. & W. F. Windle. 1938. J. Anat., 72: 344.
13. Tello, J. F. 1934. Ztschr. mik.-anat. Forsch., 36: 622.
14. Tello, J. F. 1934. Trav. Lab. Rech. Biol., Univ. Madrid, 29: 339.
15. Tello, J. F. 1935. Ibid., 30: 447.
16. Tello, J. F. 1936. Ibid., 31: 77.
17. Tello, J. F. 1938. Ibid., 32: 1.
18. Bok, S. T. 1928. in W. von Möllendorff's Handbuch mik. Anat. Mensch., 4 (1) : 478.
19. Shaner, R. F. 1932. J. Comp. Neur., 55: 493.
20. Shaner, R. F. 1934. Ibid., 60: 5.
21. Shaner, R. F. 1934. J. Anat., 68: 314.
22. Hogg, I. D. Cited by D. Hooker. 1936. Yale J. Biol. & Med., 8: 579.
23. Jasper, H. H., C. S. Bridgman & L. Carmichael. 1937. J. Exper. Psychol., 21: 63.
24. Langworthy, O. R. 1927. Contr. Emb., 19: 177.
25. Flechsig, P. 1876. Die Leitungsbahnen im Gehirn und Rückenmark des Menschen auf Grund entwickelungsgeschichtlicher Untersuchungen. W. Engelmann, Leipzig.
26. Tilney, F. & L. Casamajor. 1924. Arch. Neur. & Psychiat., 12: 1.
27. Langworthy, O. R. 1926. Contr. Emb., 17: 125.
28. Langworthy, O. R. 1928. J. Comp. Neur., 46: 201.
29. Langworthy, O. R. 1929. Contr. Emb., 20: 127.
30. Lanyworthy, O. R. 1932. Arch. Neurol. & Psychiat., 28: 1365.
31. Langworthy, O. R. 1933. Contr. Emb., 24: 3.
32. Angulo y Gonzalez, A. W. 1929. J. Comp. Neur., 48: 459.
33. Windle, W. F., M. W. Fish & J. E. O'Donnell. 1934. Ibid., 59: 139.
34. Watson, J. B. 1903. Animal Education. Univ. Chicago Press.
35. Becker, R. F., W. F. Windle, E. E. Barth & M. D. Schulz. 1940. Surg., Gyn. & Obst., 70: 603.
36. Barcroft, J. & D. H. Barron. 1937. J. Physiol., 91: 329.
37. Windle, W. F., M. Monnier & A. G. Steele. 1938. Physiol. Zool., 11: 425.
38. Windle, W. F. & R. F. Becker. 1940. Arch. Neur. & Psychiat, 43: 90.
39. Windle, W. F. 1929. J. Comp. Neur., 48: 227.
40. Henderson, Y. 1937. Science, 85: 89.
41. Zuntz, N. 1877. Pflüger's Arch., 14: 605.
42. Brown, T. G. 1915. J. Physiol., 49: 208.
43. Graham, E. A. 1913–1915. Trans. Chicago Path. Soc., 9: 123.
44. Walz, W. 1922. Monatschr. Geburt. Gyn., 60: 331.
45. Angulo y Gonzalez, A. W. 1930. Proc. Soc. Exp. Biol. & Med., 27: 579.
46. Angulo y Gonzalez, A. W. 1934. Anat. Rec., 58: Suppl. 45.
47. Windle, W. F. 1939. Physiol. Zool., 12: 39.
48. Windle, W. F. & J. Barcroft. 1938. Am. J. Physiol., 121: 684.
49. Corey, E. L. 1934. Proc. Soc. Exp. Biol. & Med., 31: 951.
50. Minkowski, M. 1923. Schweizer Arch. Neur. Psychiat., 13: 475.
51. Bolaffio, M. & G. Artom. 1926. Zeitschr. Neur. Psychiat., 103: 320.
52. Barcroft, J. & D. H. Barron. 1936. J. Physiol., 88: 56.
53. Kabat, H. & C. Dennis. Proc. Soc. Exp. Biol. & Med., 38: 864.

CHAPTER XII

FETAL MOTOR REACTIONS AND REFLEXES

MANY provisions are made during intrauterine life to assure survival after birth. A number of these depend upon development of the fetal nervous system. One function of vital importance to all species is respiration and this has been emphasized by separate consideration in another chapter. Other fundamental activities involving the somatic motor mechanisms of the body are sucking and swallowing which are well developed in all mammals at birth, crying which is encountered in most of them, and locomotion which occurs to a variable extent. In addition to these instinctive motor reactions, a number of reflexes which some have thought of as purposeful or protective have their genesis during prenatal life. The amount of functional independence attained within the uterus depends upon the degree of maturation reached in the nervous system and varies within wide limits.

DEVELOPMENT OF FEEDING REACTIONS

Coordinated movements of sucking and swallowing are fully formed in viable premature human infants, and may be seen in the common laboratory animals considerably before birth. Indeed, sucking appears to be one of the few reactions endowing the tiny newborn opossum.[1, 2] Feeding reactions may be said to begin with the first movements of the jaw.[3, 4] Opening and closing of the mouth appear in cat fetuses only about 25 mm. long, roughly comparable with the 9 weeks human. The tongue can be protruded almost this early but its sides do not curl until several days later. Similar observations have been made in guinea pigs[5] and sheep.[6] In the latter species, closure of the jaws is the only response obtained by touching the tongue between the 41st and 49th days of gestation. Throat movements occurring in brief rhythms follow jaw closure at 49 days. The tongue of the fetal sheep curls at about 70 days. These early simple activities are the forerunners of a number of more complex movements whose integration ultimately accomplish sucking, chewing and biting in the cat, sheep and guinea pig. The early components of the feeding reaction have not been thoroughly studied in human fetuses but lip movements which may be related to sucking have been seen at about 10 weeks and later.[7, 8, 9]

True sucking is rhythmical in the cat and involves a coordination or integration of tongue, lip, jaw and throat movements. Furthermore, alternate forward thrusts of the limbs and side to side head movements enter into the feeding reaction to a remarkable extent in the newborn kitten. However, the rhythmical sucking of the fetus is accomplished without participation of the limbs until late in the fetal period. Coronios[4] observed pursing of the lips around the tip of a glass stimulator in specimens 43 mm. long, and at 54 mm. the first definite sucking coordinated with head and forelimb movements was encountered. The response continues to improve and appears to be fully developed and vigorous at least one week before birth of the kitten.

The actual contractions of muscles which occur in swallowing are difficult to observe and can be seen only in late fetuses. These movements have been reported in sheep of 80 days gestation and we have seen them in the human fetus at 14 weeks. Undoubtedly they occur even earlier. When the abdominal wall of a cat fetus 25 to 30 mm. long is opened the stomach may be seen to be well filled with fluid. In specimens a little larger, brought out into the air, bubbles soon appear in this organ. This early fetal swallowing of the cat is in no way remarkable when a comparison is made with the air-breathing, sucking, 13 day "embryo" of the opossum.

Swallowing of amniotic fluid does not seem to occur under perfectly normal physiologic conditions in the fetal guinea pig until about the 42nd day of gestation. This has been demonstrated by roentgenologic studies,[10] made after injecting thorotrast into the amniotic sac (see Chapter VII). The frequency of swallowing and the amount of fluid taken into the fetal stomach increase with age. It may be concluded that the feeding mechanism, like that for respiration, has its genesis in the early part of the fetal period well in advance of the time it is normally called into use.

DEVELOPMENT OF POSTURE AND PROGRESSION

Mammalian locomotion is a complicated act requiring co-operation of many groups of muscles and exquisite integrative development within the central nervous system. Nevertheless, it too has its genesis in early prenatal life. Establishment of erect posture is prerequisite for walking. It involves the coming into action of righting reflexes; afferent impulses for these arise in the skin and muscles of the neck and body, in the labyrinths and, for higher mammals including the cat, in the retina. Maintenance of erect posture requires the presence of static or postural tonus to establish the proper neurologic balance between flexor and extensor muscle groups in order that the force of gravity be successfully opposed. After these conditions have been met, progression becomes possible by alternately and rhythmically changing the balance in such a way that flexion-extension stepping movements of the limbs are performed. Developmentally, however, the various components of a locomotor reaction are not laid down in utero in the sequence just stated.[3]

It is evident that alternation of trunk movements is fairly well developed in the fetus before there is evidence of a postural mechanism. At the time bilateral flexion of the neck and upper trunk can be induced in cat embryos less than 20 mm. long, the forelimbs move at the shoulders with the contractions of the trunk muscles. No rhythmicity manifests itself in these bilateral trunk movements before the 25 to 28 mm. stage. Active, arrhythmic alternation of the forelimbs can be induced in 30 to 35 mm. fetuses with considerable regularity; in fact, crossed extension responses begin to appear at 25 mm.

The bilateral trunk flexions, synchronized more or less passively with the limbs, are forerunners of squirming movements. Early in development the resemblance between squirming and aquatic locomotion is rather striking. At birth the kitten utilizes side to side movements in its crawling-search reaction. The reflex crossed extension following active flexor-withdrawal of one forelimb foreshadows the act of stepping. Squirming and stepping are distinct from one another until the cat fetus has reached a length of about 50 mm., at which time the first integrated activity vaguely resembling the act of crawling can be seen. Synchronized stepping movements of all four legs are not encountered before 80 mm.,[11] and even at birth the hind limbs are imperfectly coordinated with the forelimbs.[12] Rhythmicity of forelimb stepping movements improves as the time of birth approaches. Kittens 95 to 100 mm. long delivered two weeks prematurely manage to crawl very credibly.

Development of progression differs according to species in respect to late stages of development, but there is a surprising amount of similarity at first. It requires no great imagination to see a resemblance between the side to side head movements and coordinated forelimb activities by means of which the opossum

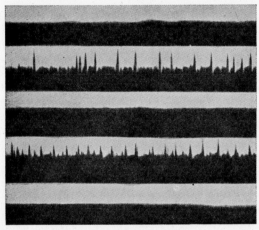

Fig. 63.—Record of muscle tonus in a sheep fetus at 144 days gestation delivered at Caesarean section with placental circulation intact. In the first, third and fifth records, the fetus lay quietly in a warm saline bath. In the second and fourth records it was lifted into the air and impulses began to flow to the muscles. (Barcroft: Irish Jour. Med. Sci., 1935.)

"embryo" reaches the mother's pouch at birth and the side to side neck, trunk and forelimb movements of the 30 mm. cat fetus. Similar reactions have been observed in rat[13, 14] and guinea pig fetuses.[5] The records are very incomplete in the human, but we have seen flexor withdrawal of one leg accompanied by crossed extension of the opposite leg in 40 mm. specimens. Rhythmicity of stepping has not been reported until much later in fetal life and even at birth behavior of a locomotor type is most ineffectual.

Development of postural tonus has not been studied thoroughly. It is probable that muscle tone as we know it in the adult is not present at all in utero under normal physiologic conditions. The fact that rhythmical respiratory movements can occur toward the end of gestation without aspiration of a significant amount of amniotic fluid demonstrates that the fetal chest is not held tonically in an elevated position which it must assume after birth.[15] The absence of afferent stimulation in utero is unquestionably an important factor in maintaining tonus at a low level.   As illustrated in Fig. 63, it was found that action potentials from fetal muscles appear when a fetus is lifted out of its warm saline bath and disappear again when it is returned to the bath.[16]   The relation of anoxemia to thresholds of nervous activity and to tonus has been discussed in the preceding chapter.

How early in prenatal life postural tonus can be induced experimentally is not definitely known, but an indication of it may be seen in cat fetuses about 50 mm. long.   It was noticed that release from their membranes was followed by straightening of the back and extension of all limbs in such a way that they appeared to stretch.   Full term birth posture, *i.e.*, extension of the head and forelimbs,[17] seem to be induced in part by a similar release of tension when the membranes burst.   A factor in development of muscle tonus may be observed in the sustained fetal movements during anoxemia.   Sustained extensor movements are sometimes so marked in cat fetuses only 30 mm. long that they resemble the decerebrate condition.

Decerebration of cat fetuses results in hyperextension of the limbs during the last three weeks of prenatal life.[3, 18]   One or two weeks before birth definite decerebrate rigidity appears in the forelegs of specimens in which the brain has been cut through from the rostral border of the mesencephalon to the rostral border of the pons.   When the level of the transection passes farther forward, leaving the region of the red nucleus intact, decerebrate rigidity fails to appear.[18, 19]   Postural tonus can be called forth in the human fetus by decerebration[20] and there too it seems to be more especially related to the midbrain and lower centers than to the higher parts of the nervous system.   Decerebrate rigidity in the rabbit after birth is illustrated in Fig. 64.

The mechanism by which the righting reaction evolves likewise has its development in the early fetus, but the actual accomplishment of righting has not been observed until after postural tonus and alternate stepping movements can be induced.[21]   Cat fetuses 75 to 100 mm. long try to hold their heads up and turn their jaws parallel to the ground when they are placed upon a flat surface. The general impression gained is that they could right themselves save for the weakness of their muscles. Between 100 and 110 mm., they are actually able to right the head in respect to the surface on which they lie, but they are completely disoriented when placed in warm water beyond their depth. No evidence of vestibular function was obtained in cat fetuses less than 110 mm. in length. Neither rotation of the specimens nor destruction of one or both labyrinths experimentally had any effect before this time. It was concluded that the vestibular right-

Fig. 64.—Decerebrate rigidity in a young rabbit. The midbrain was sectioned through the rostral border of the superior colliculus and rostral third of the pons.

ing reflex appears about the 54th day of prenatal life in the cat and that a body righting reflex precedes it by at least four days. The latter is activated by afferent impulses from the skin and deep tissues of the body and neck. Visual impulses play no part in righting reactions until some time after birth of the kitten whose eyes remain closed for several days. In the newborn kitten the vestibular righting reflex is still incompletely developed.[22]

Development of a body righting reaction before the vestibular mechanism begins to function has been confirmed in other species. In the sheep, which is more mature than the cat at birth and has a longer gestation period, righting is accomplished relatively earlier.[6]   Orientation in respect to gravity, seen in the opossum at the time of birth, which is long before the vestibular mechanism is functional, is an interesting related phenomenon.[23]

In all animals in which fetal studies have been made, three components essential for locomotion—righting, postural tonus and alternate synchronous limb movements—have been developed by the time of birth.   All three are present in some form well before the end of the gestation in most species, thus providing a factor of safety against the danger of premature interruption of intrauterine life.

DEVELOPMENT OF EYE REFLEXES

We have considered the prenatal development of motor mechanisms for respiration, feeding, posture and locomotion in some detail.   Other equally interesting fetal activities could be studied profitably, but at the present time little is known about them. Some observations on movements of the eyes and eyelids have been made but they are incomplete.

The eyeballs move behind closed lids in the fetuses of several species.   Such movements can be seen at the middle of the gestation period in guinea pigs[5] when the face is stimulated in the neighborhood of the eyes.   Somewhat later, postural changes elicit eye movements.   Reactions to light appear during the third quarter of prenatal life.   In the cat, eye movements in response to vestibular stimulation were not obtained before birth.[24]   Most kittens 5 to 7 days old showed ocular nystagmus during and after stimulation of the labyrinthine afferents by rotation.

Contraction of the orbicularis oculi muscle can be elicited in cat and guinea pig fetuses at about the middle of the gestation period.   The palpebral reflexes for protection of the eye have their genesis in these movements and are well developed in late fetal life, as can be determined by opening the eye experimentally and stimulating the cornea.   Contraction of the human orbicularis oculi was seen at about 12 weeks (40 mm.) when the eye region was touched.

Very little is known about the early development of light reflexes.   The iris of guinea pig fetuses contracts in response to light early in the last third of prenatal life.   The visual mechanism of this animal is more advanced than that of the cat or man at birth.

DEVELOPMENT OF PALMAR AND PLANTAR REFLEXES

Several investigators[7, 25, 26] have studied the movements of the digits of the hand which enter into the prehension reaction of the fetus. These constitute the palmar or grasp reflex. Hooker[26] observed flexion of the fingers but not the thumb when the palm of a human fetus of 11 weeks was touched, and it may occur even earlier. At 12 weeks the fetus formed a true fist by flexing the thumb and fingers. Later, around 16 weeks, when the fingers were held in a flexed posture stimulation of the palm brought about tightening of the fingers. Thumb movements were never as marked as those of the fingers and apposition of the thumb did not occur until after birth. Effective sustained gripping of objects with the fingers began to manifest itself around 18 weeks but even at 25 weeks it was not strong. The grasp reflex appears to have two components: finger closure and gripping.

The genesis of the human plantar reflex has interested many because of its practical importance in neurologic diagnosis. Although several have studied it in prenatal life,[25-29] Minkowski's[7, 8, 30] observations have been the most complete. Spontaneous dorsal flexion of the great toe characterized the early fetal period. No responses to stimulating the sole of the foot were obtained before 10 weeks; at this time one specimen exhibited a plantar flexion of the foot right after delivery. This was of very brief duration and when it was no longer elicitable, due to progressive asphyxiation of the specimen, only direct muscle responses could be obtained.

In fetuses of 11 to 15 weeks gestation, stimulating the sole of the foot sometimes produced dorsal flexion of the foot or of the great toe with spreading of the others. These responses, which constitute the Babinski phenomenon, were obtainable only when local anesthesia had been used and in the first few minutes of the observations. General anesthesia and progressive asphyxia led to an inversion of the response, in which the same type of stimulus brought about plantar instead of dorsal flexion. Section of the cervical spinal cord or brain stem did not alter the plantar reflexes; they could be observed for longer periods before they changed from the dorsal to the ventral type of response. There was only slight indication that higher centers participated in the dorsal form of plantar reflex before 6 months gestation.

Minkowski[8] named the early period up to 160 mm. C. H. length the neuromuscular stage; the period between 160 and 180 mm. he called the spinal stage; the period between 190 and 270 mm., the tegmento-spinal stage; and the remainder up to birth, the pallido-cerebello-tegmento-spinal stage. These divisions were set somewhat arbitrarily, for the number of observations was limited and the physiologic conditions of specimens varied to a great extent. The phenomenon of inversion of the response has been discussed in Chapter XI. The subject of plantar responses of infants and young children has been thoroughly reviewed recently by Richards and Irwin.[31]

OTHER REFLEXES

Throughout the literature, mention has been made of many other reactions and reflexes not only in experimental animals but also in human fetuses.[8] For the most part, the course of development of the skin, tendon, deep neck and other reflexes has not been followed completely and these activities do not lend themselves to significant discussion for this reason. Here are fields which future investigations may be expected to explore very profitably.

REFERENCES CITED

1. Hartman, C. G. 1920. Anat. Rec., 19: 251.
2. McCrady, E. 1938. The Embryology of the Opossum. Wistar Press, Philadelphia.
3. Windle, W. F. & A. M. Griffin. 1931. J. Comp. Neur., 52: 149.
4. Coronios, J. D. 1933. Genetic Psychol. Monog., 14: 283.
5. Carmichael, L. 1934. Ibid., 16: 337.
6. Barcroft, J. & D. H. Barron. 1939. J. Comp. Neur., 70: 477.
7. Minkowski, M. 1922. Schw. med. Wchnschr., 52: 721, 751.
8. Minkowski, M. 1938. Abderhalden's Handb. biol. Arbeitsmeth., Abt. V, Teil 5 B: 511.
9. Hooker, D. 1936. Yale J. Biol. & Med., 8: 579.
10. Becker, R. F., W. F. Windle, E. E. Barth & M. D. Schulz. 1940. Surg. Gyn. & Obst., 70: 603.
11. Brown, T. G. 1915. J. Physiol., 49: 208.
12. Tilney, F. & L. Casamajor. 1924. Arch. Neur. & Psychiat., 12: 1.
13. Swenson, E. A. 1926. Thesis, Univ. Kans.
14. Angulo y Gonzalez, A. W. 1932. J. Comp. Neur., 55: 395.
15. Henderson, Y. 1938. Adventures in Respiration, Williams & Wilkins, Baltimore.
16. Barcroft, J. 1935. Irish J. Med. Sci., Series 7, 1: 289.
17. Rudolph, L. & A. C. Ivy. 1933. Am. J. Obst. Gyn., 25: 74.

18. Windle, W. F.   1929.   J. Comp. Neur., 48: 227.
19. Langworthy, O. R.   1929.   Contrib. Emb., 20: 127.
20. Minkowski, M.   1921.   Rev. Neur., 1921: 1105, 1235.
21. Windle, W. F. & M. W. Fish.   1932.   J. Comp. Neur., 54: 85.
22. Carmichael, L.   1934.   J. Genetic Psychol., 44: 453.
23. Larsell, O., E. McCrady & A. A. Zimmermann.   1935.   J. Comp. Neur.,
        63: 95.
24. Fish, M. W. & W. F. Windle.   1932.   J. Comp. Neur., 54: 103.
25. Bolaffio, M. & G. Artom.   1924.   Arch. di Sci. Biol., 5: 457.
26. Hooker, D.   1938.   Proc. Am. Phil. Soc., 79: 597.
27. Krabbe, K.   1912.   Rev. Neurol., 24: 434.
28. Bersot, H.   1921.   Schw. Arch. Neur. & Psychiat., 8: 47.
29. Hooker, D.   1939.   Atlas of Early Human Fetal Behavior (Privately
        Printed).
30. Minkowski, M.   1926.   C. R. Cong. Med. Alienistes Neurologistes,
        Genève, 30: 301.
31. Richards, T. W. & O. C. Irwin.   1935.   Univ. Iowa Stud. Child Wel-
        fare, 11 (No. 1): 1.

CHAPTER XIII

THE FETAL SENSES

In discussing sensory mechanisms before birth the belief is not implied that the fetus is consciously aware of any sensation either in utero or after removal. Interest lies solely in whether or not the various end-organs and afferent neurons can function before birth. This is determinable by observation of the reflex motor effects of stimuli of different kinds applied to the fetus. It is seldom possible to be certain of the nature of neurons stimulated. Whether they conduct painful or tactile afferent impulses, or even whether exteroceptive or proprioceptive, following a given stimulus is usually undeterminable.

Almost everyone who has studied fetal movements has contributed information to this subject, but it is impossible to evaluate and coordinate all the data. We are faced in most instances with the task of trying to synthesize experiments performed under good and bad conditions to arrive at some knowledge of the subject. No one would think of accepting results in adult physiology of sense organs obtained in animals under narcosis and asphyxia. Yet that is the kind of data predominating in respect to the fetus.

It would seem that variations among species as well as in animals of the same species by different investigators are explainable to a very great extent on the basis of experimental methods used to study fetuses. When specimens are examined without using a general anesthetic and when they are exposed very quickly it is found that they are excitable by much milder forms of stimuli than must be used a minute or so later when anoxemia has begun to affect them.[1] Furthermore, grossly undetectable deterioration of the physiologic condition of fetuses after delivery, even when the placental circulation remains intact, affects some sensory nerves more than others and appears to alter synaptic mechanisms in such a way that motor responses change their character. These effects are especially well illustrated in human fetuses at hysterotomy performed under local anesthesia. The human fetus of the third and fourth months lies quietly within its crystal clear amnion. A very little pressure, such as follows tapping the membrane lightly, causes it to make quick jerky movements of arms, legs and other parts. When the stimulus stops, the movements stop. On the other hand, when the placenta is detached and the fetus removed from its membranes it executes "spontaneous" squirming movements which are more sustained and tonic than those seen at first. Fewer skin regions are sensitive to the lighter forms of stimulation than was the case in amnio. Excitability diminishes rapidly. Most human fetuses have been studied *after* removal from the uterus[2, 3, 4] and it was only recently that the opportunity arose to observe them at the moment of delivery while the placenta was intact and before the amnion was ruptured.[5] Consequently our knowledge of sensation in human fetuses is still very incomplete.

THE FETAL SKIN AS A RECEPTOR ORGAN

(a) PRESSURE, TOUCH AND PAIN

Motor function precedes sensibility.[6–8] In mammalian embryos it is always possible to obtain contractions of skeletal muscles by stimulating them directly before any of the sensory neurons can be activated. Spontaneous movements of the chick embryo occur in advance of the reactions which follow stimulating the surface of the body,[9, 10] but this is not the case in mammals.

The superficial epithelium with its underlying mesenchymal connective tissue serves as a receptor organ in early fetal life. Nerves course beneath the epithelium and end under it in primitive free terminations before any reflexes can be elicited in mammalian embryos.[11, 12] They appear in the face and forelimbs before they can be seen in the hind limbs and tail. Reflex responses follow stimulating them in cat embryos about 14 mm. long, but the stimuli must be somewhat stronger at that time than later. Mild faradic shocks call forth responses before it is possible to obtain them by touching the epithelium with a single hair or a soft brush. A little later, in specimens about 15 mm. or 16 mm. long, touching with a single hair often serves adequately, providing the stimulus is placed directly over a spot supplied by primitive afferent nerve fibers. Stimulation with a little brush made up of soft hairs is more often effective than a single punctate stimulus,[7, 8, 13, 14] because there is greater chance of pressing upon one of the sparse endings with it.

It is relatively easier to find reflexogenous spots upon the face than upon the limbs. Furthermore, responses to stimulating endings in the forelimb disappear before those from the face, under the influence of progressive anoxemia.[1] Consequently, the failure to elicit fetal movements by punctate stimulation of the epithelium of a limb does not prove the absence of a response-producing mechanism in the limb unless careful consideration is given to experimental conditions.

With further growth the number of nerve endings in the connective tissue beneath the epithelium increases and the fibers begin to penetrate the epithelium itself. It becomes progressively easier to find points whose stimulation elicits motor responses. Development proceeds in a cephalo-caudal direction in the body and proximo-distally in the limbs. On the other hand, rising thresholds, either in the endings themselves or in the central nervous system, soon bring about a condition of diminishing excitability of many cutaneous surfaces.[15]

One is scarcely justified in classifying the early sensory functions as touch or pain. Strictly speaking, the fetus experiences no sensation whatsoever; it simply responds automatically, reflexly, in the early part of prenatal life. It is true that the neurons are activated by external environmental changes and may be considered exteroceptive, but there is nothing about their structure and nothing about the response itself which would indicate that some subserve pain and others touch or cutaneous pressure.

It is the opinion of some investigators that both pain and touch are differentiated in late fetal life. Very little difference could be observed in cat fetuses between responses elicited by coarse but innocuous stimuli and ones which produced demonstrable trauma until after the 45th day of gestation.[7] Even at full term, pain, touch and pressure are not well differentiated. Raney and Carmichael[8] have dealt with the question of localization to tactual stimuli in relation to the genesis of space perception in the rat. They found greater specificity of response as the time of birth approached.

(b) TEMPERATURE SENSITIVITY

Only one attempt has been made to study the effect of temperature stimulation systematically throughout the entire fetal period.[16] Physiological saline solutions of different temperatures were applied in drops upon six representative cutaneous areas of guinea pig fetuses and the motor responses were recorded with a motion-picture camera. The parts stimulated were vibrissae area, ear, shoulder, rump, forepaw and hind paw. Control tests were made with the solution at body temperature. Responses were obtained throughout most of the fetal period but the warmer or cooler the solution the greater their number. Cold solutions

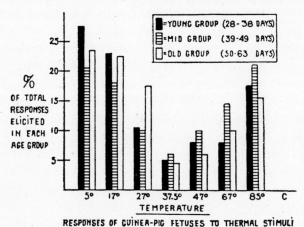

RESPONSES OF GUINEA-PIG FETUSES TO THERMAL STIMULI

Fig. 65.—Temperature sensitivity in guinea pig fetuses. (Carmichael & Lehner: J. Genetic Psychol., Vol. 50, 1937.)

appeared to be a little more effective than warm during the early part of the motile period. Sensitivity increased with age to some extent but the growth of hair modified the effectiveness of stimulation in the older specimens. Furthermore, there was evidence of sensitivity spreading from cephalic to caudal and from proximal to distal parts as development progressed. Fig. 65 illustrates the relative effectiveness of solutions of various temperatures used in three age groups of fetuses.

PROPRIOCEPTIVE FUNCTION IN THE FETUS

It is quite possible that afferent nerves of the deeper fetal tissues such as muscles and joints become functional very early. Some of the first responses of mammalian embryos may result from their activation. Movements of the primitive limbs can be induced by bending the limbs or by tapping on them. They can likewise be obtained without touching the embryos at all by tapping lightly upon the fluid filled amniotic sac containing a specimen, but one does not know what nerves are being stimulated. Since afferent neurons are present in the connective tissue just underneath the epithelium, it is just as likely that the response is due to exteroceptive as to proprioceptive stimulation.

Nevertheless there are many observations suggesting that primitive endings in the muscle are capable of being stimulated by the middle of the gestation period or a little later. The stretching of the fetus upon opening the amniotic vesicle and thus changing the pressure upon the specimen is a case in point. Other observations on the development of muscle tonus and the tonic neck and body righting reflexes leave no doubt that proprioception is present, and well formed, considerably before birth.

In newborn rats whose spinal cords were sectioned completely during intrauterine life it was often very difficult to determine by physiologic tests that nerve pathways had been interrupted. The animals responded to stimulation of points below the level of section much as did their unoperated litter mates.[17] It was suggested that in these very immature animals reflex movements below the lesion were responsible for stimulating proprioceptive endings in muscles above, setting up proprioceptive reflex movements of which the rats were aware and in this way acquainting the rats, as it were, with what was happening in a part of the body from which no direct messages could be received. The spread of activity frequently seen in much less mature mammalian fetuses of other species suggests a mechanism of a similar sort. If proprioceptive function plays a part in the responses of the early human fetus it is certain that it does not require highly specialized neuromuscular spindles because these structures do not appear until about the third month.[18]

Function of the vestibular mechanism begins rather late in fetal life of the cat.[19] In other species it may be present relatively earlier, as seems to be the case in the sheep.[15] However, caution must be exercised in attempting to determine its presence, for righting reflexes and eye movements can be induced by stimulating other receptors such as those of the neck and body. The righting reflexes have been discussed in the preceding chapter.

OLFACTORY, GUSTATORY AND VISCERAL SENSES

The olfactory apparatus is made ready during prenatal life, but it is doubtful if adequate stimuli are ever present in utero where no air comes into contact with the nasal receptors. In the newborn and prematurely born human infant, various observers have obtained evidence of olfactory function.[20, 21] It has been pointed out, however, that common chemical receptors of the trigeminal nerve are readily stimulated by strongly aromatic materials and they must not be confused with true olfactory phenomena.

Taste has been demonstrated at birth in man as well as in lower animals, but it is doubtful if differentiation between sour, salt and bitter is very well formed. The day old kitten can distinguish between milk and a mixture of milk and sodium chloride.[22] The experiments of De Snoo,[23] who injected saccharin solution into the amniotic sac of women suffering from polyhydramnios, seem to indicate that the fetus responded to the sweet taste and swallowed unusually large quantities of the amniotic fluid.

Regarding other visceral afferent stimulation, nothing is known. One can speculate that the normally occurring intestinal movements stimulate afferent neurons. Perhaps the active swallowing of amniotic fluid by fetuses in the last months of gestation is reflexly controlled by such a mechanism. Vigorous "hunger" contractions of the stomach are found in prematurely delivered mammals.[24]

HEARING AND VISION

Hearing has been considered to be imperfect at birth but seems to improve within a short time after the amniotic fluid and secretions drain from the middle ear.[25] Prematurely delivered infants show evidence of audition a little while after birth. Some investigators hold that the respiratory changes observed in the human infant concomitant with the production of sounds signify a functional auditory mechanism.

Attempts were made by Peiper[26] to observe changes in intrauterine activity associated with sound. Although it was difficult to rule out stimulation of the fetus by the mother's own responses, the evidence suggests that strong sounds may have initiated reflex movements of the fetus near term. Others have confirmed these results.[27] We have found that very slight tapping upon the amnion at the time of hysterotomy under local anesthesia results in similar quick fetal movements even at a much earlier time in prenatal life.[5] Such stimuli need not be thought of as sound producing. It is possible that the strong sounds, especially in the case of tapping upon a metal bath tub in which the pregnant woman lay, were not in themselves the cause of the fetal responses, but that pressure was transmitted to the fetus as in our own experiments. On the other hand, Sontag and Wallace have presented good evidence that the human fetus does react in utero to sound producing stimuli applied externally to the mother's abdomen. The fetal responses (movements) became more marked as term approached.[28] Electrical responses have been recorded from the fetal cochlea after auditory stimulation in guinea pigs of 52 days gestation.[29] This was the earliest period at which this species reacted overtly to such stimuli.

Although there can be no stimulation by light before birth, it is probable that the visual mechanism is functional to an imperfect degree in late prenatal life. Observations in premature infants indicate that some sort of differentiation of light and dark is present. Pupillary responses to strong light can be obtained in late fetal life.

REFERENCES CITED

1. Windle, W. F. & R. F. Becker. 1940. Arch. Neur. & Psychiat., 43: 90.
2. Minkowski, M. 1938. Abderhalden's Handb. biol. Arbeitsmeth., Abt. V, Teil 5 B: 511.
3. Bolaffio, M. & G. Artom. 1924. Arch. di Sci. Biol., 5: 457.
4. Hooker, D. 1936. Yale J. Biol. & Med., 8: 579.
5. Fitzgerald, J. E. & W. F. Windle, unpublished observations.
6. Preyer, W. 1885. Specielle Physiologie des Embryo. Grieben, Leipzig.
7. Windle, W. F. & A. M. Griffin. 1931. J. Comp. Neur., 52: 149.
8. Raney, E. T. & L. Carmichael. 1934. J. Genetic Psychol., 45: 3.
9. Orr, D. W. & W. F. Windle. 1934. J. Comp. Neur., 60: 271.
10. Kuo, Z. Y. 1932. J. Exp. Zool., 61: 395.
11. Windle, W. F. 1937. Proc. Soc. Exp. Biol. & Med., 36: 640.
12. Windle, W. F. & J. E. Fitzgerald. 1937. J. Comp. Neur., 67: 493.
13. Coronios, J. D. 1933. Genetic Psychol. Monog., 14: 283.
14. Carmichael, L. 1933. In C. Murchison's Handb. Child Psychol., 2nd ed., Clark Univ. Press, Worcester.

15. Barcroft, J. & D. H. Barron.   1939.   J. Comp. Neur., 70: 477.
16. Carmichael, L. & G. F. J. Lehner.   1937.   J. Genetic Psychol., 50: 217.
17. Hooker, D. & J. S. Nicholas.   1930.   J. Comp. Neur., 50: 413.
18. Cuajunco, F.   1927.   Contr. Emb., 19: 45.
19. Windle, W. F. & M. W. Fish.   1932.   J. Comp. Neur., 54: 85.
20. Peiper, A.   1928.   Ergebn. inn. Med. Kinderhlk., 33: 504.
21. Pratt, K. C., A. K. Nelson & K. H. Sun.   1930.   The Behavior of the
    Newborn Infant.   Ohio State Univ. Studies, No. 10.
22. Pfaffmann, C.   1936.   J. Genetic Psychol., 49: 61.
23. De Snoo, K.   1937.   Monatschr. Geburtsh. Gyn., 105: 88.
24. Carlson, A. J. & H. Ginsburg.   1915.   Am. J. Physiol., 38: 29.
25. Peterson, F. & L. H. Rainey.   1910.   Bull. N. Y. Lying-in Hosp., 7: 99.
26. Peiper, A.   1925.   Monatschr. Kinderhlk., 29: 236.
27. Forbes, H. S. & H. B. Forbes.   1927.   J. Comp. Psychol., 7: 353.
28. Sontag, L. W. and R. Wallace.   1935.   Child Development, 6: 253.
29. Rawdon-Smith, A. F., L. Carmichael and B. Wellman.   1938.   J. Exp.
    Psychol., 23: 531.

CHAPTER XIV

THE FETAL ENDOCRINE GLANDS

OUR knowledge of endocrine functions during prenatal life is fragmentary as may be expected from the fact that adult glands of internal secretion are still incompletely understood and their relationship to one another only partly determined. There seems to be little doubt that a few of the maternal hormones do influence embryonic development, but not all can pass the placental barrier.[1] The present deficiency of information concerning placental transmission of hormones is a factor limiting any discussion of their activities in the fetus. Perhaps the secretions of the fetus itself are equally or more important than those of the mother for the well being and normal metabolism of the new individual. It is with their functions that we shall be especially concerned.

THE SUPRARENAL CORTEX

Among all the endocrine glands of the human fetus, the suprarenals manifest the most remarkable peculiarities.[2, 3] Examination of them in the still-born infant reveals that they are proportionately very much larger than at any time after birth; in fact they form 0.2 per cent of the entire body weight. Those of the adult constitute only 0.01 per cent.[4] The reason for their great size is found in an hypertrophy of the innermost cortical cells forming a layer to which the names, X-zone, fetal cortex and androgenic zone have been applied. Only the outer rim of the embryonic gland differentiates into the characteristic suprarenal cortex of the adult, and it does not come into prominence until after prenatal life.

The androgenic zone of the fetal suprarenal undergoes involution rapidly after birth,[5] and as it disappears the size of the gland becomes actually as well as relatively smaller. The growth curve of the human suprarenal gland is reproduced in Fig. 66.[6] The gland loses one-third of its birth weight during the first postnatal week, one-half in the first three months and four-fifths by the end of the first year. Thereafter, a slow growth takes place and at puberty the suprarenal again attains the weight it had at the end of the fetal life; but the androgenic zone is no longer recognizable. This characteristically fetal part of the suprarenal gland has been identified in the cat,[7] mouse,[8] rabbit[9] and in one strain of rats.[10] It seems to be absent, or at least not present as a comparable distinct layer of cells, in the albino rat and some other animals.

The physiologic significance of the hypertrophied fetal cortex of the suprarenal gland is not understood. That it is closely re-

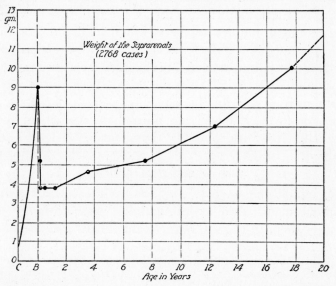

Fig. 66.—Growth of the human suprarenal glands (weight) during fetal life (C—B) and after birth. (Scammon: "The Measurement of Man," Univ. Minn. Press.)

lated to other endocrine organs is quite certain. A possible influence of maternal sex hormones upon the growing fetal suprarenal is suggested by the closely parallel growth curve of the uterus in prenatal and early postnatal life (Fig. 67) . Involution of the X-zone of young male mice is accomplished under the influence of testicular hormone.[11]

It has been suggested that the fetal suprarenal gland elaborates an andromimetic substance.[12, 13] Its ability to maintain the prostates of the castrated immature mouse and rat, which degenerate when gonads and suprarenals are removed, demonstrates an andromimetic property quite clearly.[14, 15] Recently, however, evidence has been advanced which indicates that carefully prepared extracts of fetal and of other X-zone-bearing glands do not have androgenic properties,[16] but it is possible that the amount of suprarenal tissue extracted was too small to produce effects. Should it prove that androgens are lacking, one would have to discard the attractive hypothesis that the androgenic cortex serves directly to protect the fetus against an excessive influence of maternal estrogens reaching it through the placental barrier.

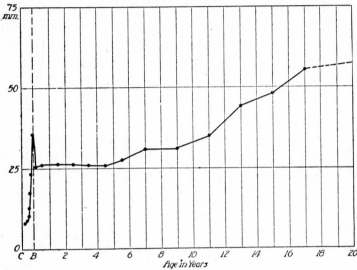

Fig. 67.—Growth of the human uterus (length) during fetal life (C—B) and after birth. (Scammon: "The Measurement of Man," Univ. Minn. Press.)

The possibility that cortin or a cortin-like hormone is formed by the fetal suprarenal gland has received attention. Some investigators have reported that the survival times of adrenalectomized cats and dogs are prolonged during advanced pregnancy.[17–19] Others failed to substantiate this at the end of gestation,[20] but even if it is true there is no proof that a fetal secretion protected the mother. Progesterone maintains life and growth in ferrets and rats in the absence of suprarenal glands,[21–23] and the functional corpus luteum of pregnant adrenalectomized animals does the same.[24] Adrenalectomy of pregnant rats during gestation results in an increase in weight of the fetal glands[25] as will be seen in Table 22.

13

TABLE 22

THE EFFECTS OF ADRENALECTOMY DURING PREGNANCY UPON THE WEIGHTS OF THE FETAL SUPRARENAL GLANDS

Time of adrenalectomy of mother	No. of litters	Average wt. of fetuses (gm.)		Ave. wt. of suprarenal glands of fetuses (mg.)	
		♂	♀	♂	♀
Unoperated controls......	18	5.34	5.03	0.90	0.82
14th day of gestation.....	15	4.96	4.78	1.23	1.18
7th day of gestation......	10	4.70	4.51	1.17	1.13

Attempts have been made to destroy the suprarenal glands by means of intrauterine surgery to observe effects on other fetal endocrine organs,[26] but it proved impossible to obtain clear-cut results because of the magnitude of technical difficulties.

THE SUPRARENAL MEDULLA

The medulla of the suprarenal gland has an embryonic origin very different from that of the cortex. It is formed by cells which arise from the primordia of sympathetic ganglia and which begin to migrate into the already prominent cortical bodies at about seven weeks gestation in man. Cells of the suprarenal medulla as well as of certain other small glandular bodies of similar embryonic origin (*e.g.,* the aortic paraganglia) possess a remarkable affinity for chrome compounds with which they take on a brown color. This chromaffin reaction has been demonstrated to be elicitable first at about the time extracts of embryonic suprarenal tissue begin to produce pharmacologic responses characteristic of epinephrin.[27-29]

Many have investigated the activities of the embryonic and fetal suprarenal medulla by this histochemical method as well as by other chemical and sensitive physiologic techniques. Epinephrin-like reactions are obtainable from suprarenal extracts prepared from chick embryos as early as the eighth day of incubation although similar extracts of other embryonic tissues give negative results.[29-31] Epinephrin is formed, or at least stored, in the medulla of the glands in many fetal mammals before the middle of gestation.[32-39] The medullary cells show the chromaffin reaction at the 17th to 18th day in the pig and both physiologic and histochemical tests reveal the presence of an epinephrin-like substance at the time migration of medullary cells into the cortical bodies is first observable.[28, 29] The epinephrin content of fetal glands has been reported to be greater than in the adult; more was found in female than in male fetuses.[35] A correlation between appearance of epinephrin in the suprarenal of the rat and the origin of fetal movements has been suggested,[40] but this seems to be coincidental.

In sharp contrast with results obtained in most mammals, human fetal suprarenal extracts give negative or only very slightly positive tests for epinephrin.[36–39, 41–44] However, in full term infants as well as prematures which lived for a short time somewhat more definite reactions were obtained. The near failure to obtain epinephrin-like responses from human fetal suprarenal extracts may be contrasted with the observation that the paraganglia yielded definite amounts of epinephrin in one instance:[43]

Human suprarenal at birth = 0.01 mg. epinephrin per 2.7 gm. gland.
Human paraganglion at birth = 0.24 mg. epinephrin per 0.11 gm. gland.

Any relationship between low content of epinephrin and the presence of a very prominent androgenic cortical zone in man is undetermined.

THE SEX HORMONES

An excellent consideration of embryologic development of sex with a review of all but the latest literature has appeared recently.[45] We are limited here to only a small part of this interesting subject.

The male gonads produce substances with androgenic properties in prenatal life. It was demonstrated that extracts prepared from the testes of fetal calves are similar to those from the adult and the hormonal yield per unit weight of tissue is greater.[46] It is probable that the male sex glands begin to elaborate secretions about as soon as their sex can be differentiated, which is the sixth day in the incubating chick and the seventh week in man. The ovary is recognizable as such about a week later than the testes.

The best indication we have that fetal androgens are active in early prenatal life is that forthcoming from a study of freemartins in cattle.[47, 48] The freemartin is an intersexed or masculinized female calf which develops under conditions of chorionic fusion in which vascular anastomoses are established between the placentas of adjacent male and female fetuses. The male is always a normal individual. It is believed that the hormone elaborated by the fetal male gonads circulates in the conjoined blood streams, acting upon the female twin's Müllerian or female duct derivatives to inhibit their normal development and upon its Wolffian or masculine duct derivatives to stimulate their abnormal differentiation. When vascular connections are not established between adjacent fetuses of opposite sex no freemartin results, but the calves are normal male and female.

A similar freemartin condition has been described in swine.[49] It should be noted that the placentas of both cattle and swine are relatively inefficient from the standpoint of permeability. A high degree of placental fusion, apparently with vascular union, was observed in one instance of synchorial twinning in the cat.[50] The fetuses were of opposite sexes, were sexually normal in every way, and were sufficiently advanced in development to make it appear certain that the female twin would not have become a freemartin. Similarly synchorial twins of opposite sexes are encountered in other animals and man,[51, 52] but freemartins have not been reported. It will probably be profitable to learn how the transmission of fetal male sex hormones across the placental barrier is related to the phenomenon in question. It is difficult to see how the freemartin condition can be so limited unless the diffusibility of embryonic testicular hormones is greater in the deciduate types of placentas which therefore never allow hormones to accumulate in sufficient amounts to stimulate the Wolffian derivatives of the genetically female twin.

It would carry us too far afield to inquire deeply into the extensive experimental studies on production of pseudohermaphrodism in the lower animals.[45] Success has been attained in mammals at several laboratories recently.[53] Injections of pregnant rats with large doses of testosterone and related preparations bring about abnormal development of the potentially male ducts of genetically female young. It is necessary to administer the hormone before the 16th day of gestation to obtain the most marked effects.[54] This is about one day before the Wolffian ducts begin to regress. The intersexed individuals produced experimentally resemble the naturally occurring freemartins in certain particulars.

Male offspring of rats receiving large doses of estrogens before the 13th day of gestation have been markedly feminized.[55] Thus a converse of nature's freemartin has been induced with excessive female sex hormones. The extent to which the mother's own hormones may influence normal development of sex in the fetus is not understood. It is known that the fetal uterus exhibits a marked hypertrophy and diminishes in size after intimate contact with the mother is abolished by birth. The mammary glands of newborn infants of both sexes show enlargement and may secrete transiently. It is possible that this production of "witch milk" is stimulated by the same maternal hormonal mechanism that leads to the preparation of the mother's breasts for lactation.

THE THYROID GLAND

The ability of the fetal thyroid to secrete at an early period seems to have been established. Iodine has been identified in the gland at the 2nd or 3rd month of gestation in cattle, sheep and swine[33] and in man at least as early as the 6th month.[56] The amount is said to increase toward the end of prenatal life but to be low as compared with the adult gland, perhaps because storage of colloid is not so marked in the fetus.[57] There is no close correlation between the maternal and fetal blood content of hormone iodine, a fact which suggests that the fetus is secreting its own hormone.[58] The presence of thyreoglobulin in the human fetus at the 3rd and 4th months has been established by means of an immunologic precipitin reaction.[59]

Amphibian metamorphosis and growth can be influenced by extracts and transplants of avian and mammalian fetal thyroid glands. In general, it may be said that the thyroid becomes active at about the time its structure begins to resemble that of the adult. This is on the 11th day of incubation in the chick.[60] In calves colloid is present as early as the 2nd[61] and differentiation is completed between the 4th and 6th prenatal months; at this time extracts serve to bring about metamorphosis in the axolotl, a salamander which normally retains the larval state throughout life.[30] Extracts prepared from the glands of pig fetuses 7 cm. long proved to be inactive, but those from 9 cm. pig fetuses produced reactions comparable with adult thyroids; correlatively, the adult structure was nearly attained at 9 cm.[62] When bits of the thyroid gland from a 3-months-old human fetus (10 cm. C. R. length) were transplanted into larvae of a toad, accelerated development took place, and transplants from 5-months-old human fetuses had more marked effects.[63]   Control experiments with bits of fetal muscle gave negative results.   It was found that the thyroid gland of the younger fetus had already developed colloid filled vesicles.

Little is known about placental transmission of the thyroid secretions.   In swine, horses, cattle and sheep, animals with adeciduate placentas, it appears that there is no transmission.   In geographical regions where iodine deficiency is prevalent the off-spring of these animals are born in a state of athyreosis while the mothers show little or no evidence of the iodine lack.[64, 65]   It seems that the fetal requirements of iodine are greater than those of the mother and that the fetus cannot draw upon the mother's hormone but must manufacture its own.   Iodine feeding during pregnancy corrects this deficiency, and the newborn pigs are then normal.   In man, on the other hand, it seems probable that the mother's hormone is available to the fetus because it can traverse the placental barrier.   Human infants born without or with atrophic thyroid glands exhibit none of the symptoms of myxedema, but a latent athyreosis soon manifests itself.[66–71]

THE PARATHYROID GLANDS

Practically nothing is known of function of fetal parathyroid glands.   Injections of parathyroid hormone into dog fetuses bring on an elevation of the calcium level of the fetal, but not the maternal blood.   This suggests that the parathyroid secretion does not pass the placenta in the species studied.[72]   Attempts have been made to determine the effects of fetal glands of dogs after thyroparathyroidectomy of the mothers.   It was found that tetany developed just as soon as it did in nonpregnant animals.[73, 74]

THE THYMUS

Although the thymus is usually considered with the glands of internal secretion, it is doubtful if it logically belongs there.   By 3 months in man, the thymus has the appearance of a lymphoid organ with cortex and medulla already in evidence.   There is no anatomical basis for the belief that the gland elaborates a hormone and few attempts have been made to study the fetal thymus from the standpoint of its endocrine function.[36, 75, 76]

Extracts of thymus seem to exert no effects when fed to tadpoles, although opinion has been divided on this question.[77, 78] An extract of calf thymus, to which the name "thymocrescin" was given, has been reported to produce marked acceleration of growth in young rats when injected in daily doses as small as 1 mg.[79]

Another extract prepared in an entirely different way resulted in even more marked effects in the hands of Rowntree and his colleagues.[80] This material was injected intraperitoneally in 1 cc. doses into rats over long periods including gestation and lactation; the young of succeeding generations were similarly treated. Effects on the offspring of the first animals were not significant but the second and subsequent generations showed remarkable changes. They were larger at birth, more of them survived and their postnatal development was definitely speeded. The young rats became sexually mature precociously. Maximum effects were found in the eighth and tenth generations. It was necessary to keep giving the treatments and not miss a generation or the effects were promptly dissipated. From the more recent reports it seems that it was necessary to inject the extracts into females only.[81]

Other investigators have attempted to reproduce these very interesting results, but so far no adequate confirmation has been reported.[82] The biologic effects of certain iodine-reducing substances (glutathione, ascorbic acid, cysteine) have been found to simulate those of the thymus extracts in certain particulars.[81]

THE HYPOPHYSIS

A few studies have been made on placental transmission of hypophyseal extracts but we know little about hormone elaboration by the fetus itself. When pituitrin was injected into rabbit fetuses no muscular contractions were observed in the mother.[83] This suggests, but does not prove, that the substance failed to pass the placenta. Anterior lobe extract did not produce any evidence of its usual gonadotropic activity in the mother when it was introduced into the fetuses.[84] Furthermore, this hormone failed to appear in the fetal fluids after it had been injected into the mother; at least, the administration of these fluids to other adult rabbits failed to bring about ovulatory changes.[85] These experiments seem to show that there is very little if any transmission of the large molecules of the anterior lobe gonadotropic factor even in the hemo-endothelial type of placenta.

The fetal hypophysis seems to be capable of elaborating several active principles.[35, 86–89] A pressor substance has been found at 6 months in man. Similar studies have been made in fetuses of cattle, sheep and swine in which the response was found relatively earlier. The guinea pig uterine strip method served to demonstrate the oxytocic principle about as early as the pituitary gland can be recognized macroscopically. It was found in appreciable amounts in pigs and sheep at term.

The melanophore-expanding hormone has been identified in the fetal hypophysis. It was found in the glands from calf fetuses of 3 months gestation but was not there at 2 months. It was present in pigs of only 30 mm. C. R. length.[30, 88]

Gonadotropic and growth promoting factors of the anterior lobe seem to make their appearance rather late in fetal life, and the former is later than the latter.[90] In fetal pigs the gonadotropic response was obtained from glands at the 20 to 21 cm. stage, a short time before the end of gestation but was not found earlier. The general body growth response could be obtained at the 9 to 13 cm. stage which was just about the same time the thyroid hormone made its appearance.[62, 90]

SECRETIN

Extracts of the proximal portion of the fetal small intestine have been found to cause secretion of pancreatic juice when injected into adult animals with pancreatic fistulas.[91–94] The earliest period at which secretin has been obtained from the human fetus is 4½ months. The exact source of the hormone is unknown and attempts to ascribe it to the chromaffin cells of the duodenum[95] seem to be entirely unjustified.

THE ENDOCRINE PANCREAS

The endocrine function of the pancreas is vested in the cells of the islands of Langerhans. These make their appearance in the third month of human gestation but it is not known how early they become capable of secreting. The acinar portion of the gland does not begin to produce its proteolytic ferment before about the 5th month,[96] and Banting and Best took advantage of the fact that island tissue is functional earlier when they chose the pancreas of the fetal calf as a source of antidiabetic principle in their early search for insulin.[97] Many have discussed the possibility that fetal insulin plays an important rôle in carbohydrate metabolism of the fetus and have pointed to a correlation between the appearance of glycogen in the liver and the development of island tissue in the pancreas,[98, 99] but the relationship is still somewhat unsatisfactorily established because the influence of maternal secretion acting through the placenta is difficult to evaluate. It is said not to pass the placenta from fetal to maternal sides.[83] Administration of insulin to pregnant cats failed to reduce the blood sugar level of the fetuses near term. This suggests that the placenta is impervious at the time, but at earlier stages similar results were not obtained.[100] Further discussion of this question will be found in Chapter XV.

In birds, where all metabolic processes must be managed by the fetus itself, an insulin-like substance has been found in the unincubated egg.[101] However, it is not present in the tissues of the early chick embryo until after the pancreatic islets are formed.

The offspring of diabetic animals are not diabetic and as a rule seem to possess healthy glands.[102] This is not always true in man where hypertrophy and hyperplasia of islands and postpartum hypoglycemic deaths are encountered in infants born of diabetic women.[103] Although hyperplastic pancreatic islands are not found in all instances, careful searching might show the condition to be more prevalent.

The possibility that during prenatal life fetal insulin can protect the diabetic mother has been discussed by several investigators. It was discovered by Carlson and his colleagues[104, 105] that the urine of completely pancreatectomized dogs remained free from sugar when the operation was performed in late stages of pregnancy. This suggested that fetal island tissue had supported both the mother and fetuses, for after parturition the mother exhibited glycosuria. These experiments have been adequately confirmed[106] and similar conditions apparently occur in the human.[107] Completely depancreatized dogs maintained in good health by diet and insulin therapy can conceive and give birth to normal pups. They show an increased carbohydrate tolerance for only about two weeks prior to labor. However, an even greater tolerance appears after birth during lactation; it would seem that the results previously ascribed entirely to fetal insulin are more probably due largely to increased utilization of carbohydrates by the fetuses and, after birth, by the nursing puppies. We cannot be sure that the fetal insulin plays any part in protecting the diabetic mother. It is quite reasonable to suppose that it is more important for the utilization of sugar received by the fetus from the mother.

Glycogen appears in the liver of the developing chick at 7 days of incubation. This is about three days before definitive islands of Langerhans make their appearance. Between the tenth and thirteenth days the glycogen content of liver cells diminishes and the metabolic rate and respiratory quotient increase, although there is no rise in the blood sugar concentration. Thus it appears that an increased utilization of carbohydrate by the embryo is correlated with the advent of function in suprarenal medulla, pancreatic islands and thyroid glands.[108]

REFERENCES CITED

1. Needham, J. 1931. Chemical Embryology, Macmillan, N. Y.
2. Grollman, A. 1936. The Adrenals, Williams & Wilkins, Baltimore.
3. Rogoff, J. M. 1932. Chap. 23, vol. 2 in Cowdry: Special Cytology, Hoeber, N. Y.
4. Scammon, R. E. 1923. Chap. 3, vol. 1 in Abt: Pediatrics, Saunders, Philadelphia.
5. Elliott, T. R. & R. G. Armour. 1911. J. Path. & Bact., 15: 481.
6. Scammon, R. E. 1930. Pt. IV in The Measurement of Man. Univ. of Minn. Press, Minneapolis.
7. Davies, S. 1937. Quart. J. Mic. Sci., 80: 81.
8. Howard-Miller, E. 1927. Am. J. Anat., 40: 251.
9. Roaf, R. 1935. J. Anat., 70: 126.
10. Bacsich, P. & S. J. Folley. 1939. J. Anat., 73: 432.
11. Martin, S. J. 1930. Proc. Soc. Exp. Biol. & Med., 28: 41.
12. Reichstein, T. 1936. Helv. Chi. Acta, 19: 223.
13. Howard, E. 1937. Am. J. Physiol., 119: 339.
14. Burrill, M. W. & R. R. Greene. 1939. Proc. Soc. Exp. Biol. & Med., 40: 327.
15. Howard, E. 1939. Am. J. Anat., 65: 105.
16. Gersh, I. & A. Grollman. 1939. Am. J. Physiol., 126: 368.
17. Steward, H. A. 1913. Proc. 17th Internat. Cong. Med., Sect. 3, Pt. 2, p. 173.

18. Stewart, G. N. & J. M. Rogoff. 1925. Proc. Soc. Exp. Biol. & Med., 22: 394 and 23: 190.
19. Rogoff, J. M. & G. N. Stewart. 1927. Am. J. Physiol., 79: 508.
20. Corey, E. L. 1927. Proc. Soc. Exp. Biol. & Med., 25: 167.
21. Gaunt, R., W. O. Nelson & E. Loomis. 1938. Ibid., 39: 319.
22. Gaunt, R. & H. W. Hays. 1938. Science, 88: 576.
23. Greene, R. R., J. A. Wells & A. C. Ivy. 1939. Proc. Soc. Exp. Biol. & Med., 40: 83.
24. Rogoff, J. M. & G. N. Stewart. 1929. Am. J. Physiol., 88: 162.
25. Ingle, D. J. & G. T. Fisher. 1938. Proc. Soc. Exp. Biol. & Med., 39: 149.
26. Tobin, C. E. 1939. Am. J. Anat., 65: 151.
27. Weymann, M. F. 1922. Anat. Rec., 24: 299.
28. Howard-Miller, E. 1926. Am. J. Physiol., 75: 267.
29. Okuda, M. 1928. Endocrin., 12: 342.
30. Hogben, L. T. & F. A. E. Crew. 1923. Brit. J. Exp. Biol., 1: 1.
31. Lutz, B. R. and M. A. Case. 1925. Am. J. Physiol., 73: 670.
32. Langlois, J. P. and J. Rehns. 1899. Comp. Rend. Soc. Biol., 51: 146.
33. Fenger, F. 1912. J. Biol. Chem., 11: 489 and 12: 55.
34. Cevolotto, G. 1916. Chem. Abstr., 10: 1212.
35. McCord, C. P. 1915. J. Biol. Chem., 23: 435.
36. Svehla, K. 1900. Arch. exp. Path. u. Pharm., 43: 321.
37. Moore, B. & C. O. Purinton. 1900. Am. J. Physiol., 4: 57.
38. Lewis, J. H. 1916. J. Biol. Chem., 24: 249.
39. Saito, S. 1929. Tohoku J. Exp. Med., 12: 254.
40. Pankratz, D. S. 1931. Anat. Rec., 49: 31.
41. Ingier, A. & G. Schmorl. 1911. Münch. med. Wochenschr., 1911, 2405 (Abstr.).
42. Samelson, P. 1912. Ztschr. f. Kinderhlk., 3: 65.
43. Elliott, T. R. Personal to G. Barger, 1914. The Simpler Natural Bases, Longmans, Green, London (p. 93).
44. Kramer, D. 1918. Monatschr. f. Kinderhlk., 14: 531.
45. Willier, B. H. 1939. Chap. 3 in E. Allen's "Sex and Internal Secretions," Williams & Wilkins, Baltimore.
46. Womack, E. B. & F. C. Koch. 1931. Proc. 2nd Internat. Cong. Sex Res., 1930, p. 329.
47. Lillie, F. R. 1917. J. Exp. Zool., 23: 371.
48. Lillie, F. R. 1923. Biol. Bull., 44: 47.
49. Hughes, W. 1929. Anat. Rec., 41: 213.
50. Wislocki, G. B. & G. W. D. Hamlett. 1934. Ibid., 61: 97.
51. Hamlett, G. W. D. & G. B. Wislocki. 1934. Ibid., 61: 81.
52. Wislocki, G. B. 1939. Am. J. Anat., 64: 445.
53. Greene, R. R., M. W. Burrill & A. C. Ivy. 1938. Am. J. Obst. & Gyn., 36: 1038.
54. Burrill, M. W. & R. R. Greene. 1939. Am. J. Physiol., 126: 452.
55. Greene, R. R. & M. W. Burrill. 1939. Ibid., 126: 510.
56. Nosaka, T. 1927. Chem. Abs., 21: 3913.
57. Maurer, E. 1927. Ztschr. f. Kinderhlk., 43: 163.
58. McClendon, J. F. & C. E. McLennan. 1939. Proc. Soc. Exp. Biol. & Med., 40: 553.
59. Hektoen, L. & K. Schulhof. 1925. Proc. Natl. Acad. Sci., 11: 481.

60. Willier, B. H. Personal to J. Needham. 1931. Chem. Emb., Macmillan, N. Y.
61. Abbott, A. C. & J. Prendergast. 1937. Can. Med. Assoc. J., 36: 228.
62. Rumph, P. & P. E. Smith. 1926. Anat. Rec., 33: 289.
63. Schulze, W., W. Schmitt & K. Hölldobler. 1928. Endokrin., 2: 2.
64. Smith, G. E. & H. Welch. 1917. J. Biol. Chem., 29: 215.
65. Smith, G. E. 1919. Endocrin., 3: 262.
66. Siegert. 1921. Verh. deuts. Gesel. Kinderhlk., 22: 364.
67. Kocher, T. 1892. Deuts. Ztschr. Chirurg., 34: 556.
68. Wegelin, C. & J. Abelin. 1921. Arch. exp. Path. u. Pharm., 89: 219.
69. Thomas, E. & E. Delhougne. 1924. Virchow's Arch. path. Anat. u. Physiol., 248: 201.
70. Kraus, E. J. 1929. Beitr. path. Anat. allg. Path., 82: 291.
71. Sgalitzer, K. 1938. Ibid., 100: 285.
72. Hoskins, F. M. & F. F. Snyder. 1927. Proc. Soc. Exp. Biol. & Med., 25: 264.
73. Vassale, G. 1905. Arch. ital. biol., 43: 177.
74. Werelius, A. 1913. Surg. Gyn. & Obst., 16: 141.
75. Trinka, L. 1914. Publ. biol. École Hautes Études Vét. de Brno (in Czech; cited by J. Needham, 1931).
76. Macchiarulo, O. 1930. Riv. ital. di Gin., 11: 357.
77. Gudernatsch, J. F. 1914. Am. J. Anat., 15: 431.
78. Allen, B. M. 1920. J. Exp. Zool., 30: 189.
79. Asher, L. 1938. Abderhalden's Handb. biol. Arbeitsmethod. Abt. 5, Teil 3B (2): 929.
80. Rowntree, L. G., J. H. Clark & A. M. Hanson. 1934. Science, 80: 274.
81. Rowntree, L. G., A. Steinberg, N. H. Einhorn & N. K. Schaffer. 1938. Endocrin., 23: 584.
82. Nelson, W. O. 1939. Chap. 21, in E. Allen's "Sex and Internal Secretions," Williams & Wilkins, Baltimore.
83. Snyder, F. F. & F. M. Hoskins. 1927. Anat. Rec., 35: 23.
84. Wislocki, G. B. & F. F. Snyder. 1932. Proc. Soc. Exp. Biol. & Med., 30: 196.
85. Goodman, L. & G. B. Wislocki. 1933. Am. J. Physiol., 106: 323.
86. Schlimpert, H. 1913. Monatschr. Geb. u. Gyn., 38: 8.
87. Lewis, D. 1916. J. Exp. Med., 23: 677.
88. Snyder, F. F. 1928. Am. J. Anat., 41: 399.
89. Bell, G. H. & J. M. Robson. 1937. Quart. J. Exp. Physiol., 27: 205.
90. Smith, P. & C. Dortzbach. 1929. Anat. Rec., 43: 277.
91. Hallion, L. & P. Lequeux. 1906. Comp. rend. Soc. Biol., 61: 33.
92. Camus, L. 1906. Ibid., 61: 59.
93. Pringle, H. 1911. J. Physiol., 42: 40 P.
94. Koschtojanz, C. 1931. Pflüger's Arch., 227: 359.
95. Parat, M. 1924. Comp. rend. Soc. Biol., 90: 1023.
96. Ibrahim, J. 1909. Biochem. Ztschr., 22: 24.
97. Banting, F. G. & C. H. Best. 1922. J. Lab. & Clin. Med., 7: 464.
98. Aron, M. 1923. Comp. rend. Soc. Biol., 89: 187, 189.
99. Potvin, R. & M. Aron. 1927. Comp. rend. Soc. Biol., 96: 267.
100. Britton, S. W. 1930. Am. J. Physiol., 95: 178.
101. Shikinami, Y. 1928. Tohoku J. Exp. Med., 10: 1.

102. Joslin, E. P.   1915.   Boston Med. & Surg. J., 173: 841.
103. Smyth, F. S. & M. B. Olney.   1938.   J. Pediat., 13: 772.
104. Carlson, A. J. & F. M. Drennan.   1911.   Am. J. Physiol., 28: 391.
105. Carlson, A. J., J. S. Orr & W. S. Jones.   1914.   J. Biol. Chem., 17: 19.
106. Cuthbert, F. P., A. C. Ivy, B. L. Isaacs & J. Gray.   1936.   Am. J. Physiol.,
      115: 480.
107. Lawrence, R. D.   1929.   Quart. J. Med., 22: 191.
108. Dalton, A. J.   1937.   Anat. Rec., 68: 393.

CHAPTER XV

FETAL NUTRITION AND METABOLISM

PARAPLACENTAL NUTRITION

THE maternal organism not only breathes and excretes for the fetus but it also digests food and furnishes nutriments needed for the growth of the new individual. In early stages of development the intimacy between embryo and mother is slight, and until a close approximation to the endometrium is effected nutrition can not be accomplished by direct processes which characterize the older and more advanced types of placental circulatory systems. An intermediate substance of transient nutritional value to the early embryo is provided by secretion of the uterine glands, by transudation and especially by erosion of the endometrium and production of tissue detritus in response to implantation of the newly arrived blastocyst. To this paraplacental nutriment, the name histotrophe may be applied.[1-4]

In mammals with relatively simple epithelio-chorial and syndesmo-chorial placentas, such as the horse and sheep, quite a different histotrophic material bathes the chorionic surface throughout gestation. This, the "uterine milk," is composed predominantly of secretions and transudates from the intact uterine epithelium. Its high fat content gives it the appearance of dilute milk.

It is doubtful if histotrophic nutrition can be of real significance in man and other primates for more than a few days during implantation.[5] A yolk-sac placenta develops early in the rat, and with it a more efficient mechanism for nutrition. The passage of substances through the yolk-sac epithelium of the rat has been demonstrated very clearly.[6, 7] One can not consider that the processes involved are entirely histotrophic in those animals in which uterine milk is lacking.

With the formation of endothelio-chorial, hemo-chorial and hemo-endothelial (deciduate) placentas in carnivores, primates and rodents, histotrophe plays only a minor and transient part and nutrition becomes possible largely by processes similar to those occurring in the tissues of the body itself. The substances which pass more directly from one blood stream to the other have been designated hemotrophe. Thus Bonet's term "embryotrophe" has given way to a more useful classification:

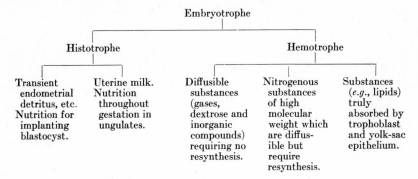

Embryotrophe				
Histotrophe		**Hemotrophe**		
Transient endometrial detritus, etc. Nutrition for implanting blastocyst.	Uterine milk. Nutrition throughout gestation in ungulates.	Diffusible substances (gases, dextrose and inorganic compounds) requiring no resynthesis.	Nitrogenous substances of high molecular weight which are diffusible but require resynthesis.	Substances (*e.g.*, lipids) truly absorbed by trophoblast and yolk-sac epithelium.

PLACENTAL PERMEABILITY

Nutrition of the fetus is closely dependent upon the manner and efficiency with which materials are transmitted across the placental barrier. It must be born in mind that the physiologic characteristics of the placenta are not constant throughout development, nor are they the same in all species of mammals. Furthermore, the chorio-allantoic attachment is not the only means of contact between the fetus and mother; in some species, *e.g.*, the rat, a yolk-sac placenta of very different structure is known to serve concomitantly throughout gestation.[7] The term "the placenta" refers as a rule to the combined ectoplacenta and yolk-sac placenta when used in reference to function. Density and number of tissue layers separating maternal and fetal blood streams vary, as was pointed out in Chapter I. For these reasons one must exercise caution in attempting to draw conclusions regarding the permeability of one type of placenta based upon experiments with a different type.

The subject of placental permeability is much too extensive to be discussed in detail, but a few significant observations can be considered. Such observations inquire into the characteristics of materials which make their way across the living membranes, and into the nature of the processes involved in their passage.

Particulate matter, even when microscopic in size, fails to pass the most advanced hemo-endothelial placentas. Formerly there was much discussion of this, but the fact is now well established.[8] Certain ultra-microscopic particles in colloidal solutions do pass, and the dye trypan blue seems to be one lying on the borderline between the transmissible and non-transmissible substances in the hemo-endothelial placentas. This dye does not traverse the endothelio-chorial type found in the cat.[9]

That a relationship exists between the molecular weight of substances and their ability to pass through placentas can scarcely be doubted. Oxygen, carbon dioxide and many chemical compounds of low molecular weight traverse membranes of all placentas. Tabulation of data available up to 1931 will be found in Needham's[10] "Chemical Embryology" (Table 227). From this it appears that the thinner the barrier, the more permeable it is to materials of large molecular size. On the other hand, it has been demonstrated that the thin chorionic trophoblast plates of the early rat placenta are actually less permeable than the much thicker yolk-sac epithelium to the dye, toluidin blue.

A very close parallelism exists between the ability of colloidal dye solutions to diffuse in films of 20 to 30 per cent gelatin and the efficiency of their transmission from the mother to the fetuses of rats and mice.[11] These and other observations[10] have frequently been cited as evidence that the placenta acts largely in the capacity of an ultra-filter. There is ample evidence, however, that the fat solubility of materials in the blood streams, their pH and ionic charges at the membrane play important rôles in governing placental permeability. Furthermore, one can not tell whether the experiments with colloidal dyes demonstrate passage through the ectoplacenta, the yolk-sac placenta or a combination of both.

Although a number of investigations have led to the conclusion that species differences exist at term in respect to permeability of dye solutions,[9] other chemical solutions[12] and antibodies,[13] few experiments have been concerned with the changes taking place throughout the course of development of any one species. Recently, however, it was demonstrated that the permeability of the rabbit's placenta to agglutinins and hemolysins increases during the course of gestation.[14] The ratio of the titre of the fetuses to that of the mother plotted against the gestation age forms a sigmoid curve (Fig. 68). Permeability is clearly related to the changing histologic structure of the placenta during gestation.[15]

The two principal theories concerning the nature of the placental barrier merit further study.   Many recent observers have favored the view that it is essentially an inert semipermeable membrane, but advocates of the concept of a vital function are not lacking.   A preformed regulatory mechanism, inferring a secretory process, has been suggested.[16]

Those who favor the ultra-filter theory believe that substances pass from mother to fetus, or in the reverse direction, by diffusion and filtration, that physical processes alone govern the transmis-

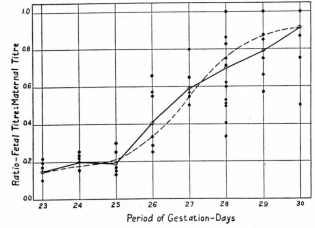

Fig. 68.—Permeability of the rabbit placenta to antibodies at different times during prenatal life.   (Rodolfo: J. Exp. Zool., Vol. 68, 1934.)

sion and that molecular size plays an important part in determining which shall and which shall not cross the barrier.[10, 11, 17, 18] This seems to be well established for gases, dextrose and a number of chemical compounds of relatively low molecular weight, including some of the products of fetal metabolism.   The subject has been reviewed by Schlossman[19] who concludes that, aside from endocrine activities, there is not the slightest reason to believe that the placenta and its chorionic epithelium has a truly secretory function.   He believes that even in the instances of seemingly vitalistic activities, physical principles in the last analysis can explain transmission.   Nevertheless it is reasonable to adhere to the concept of absorption in the trophoblast.   The recent studies on

14

metabolism of lipids provide strong circumstantial evidence for the vitalistic theory.[46]

With the recognition of functional properties of the yolk-sac in some animals, the question of secretory function takes on renewed interest. In structure as well as in physiologic reaction to perfusion of the maternal blood vessels with various chemical and dye solutions, the yolk-sac placenta of the rat appears to be an organ for absorption.[6, 7] When more attention has been paid to the functions of this organ, as well as to factors of age and species differences, our knowledge of the passage of the nutriment from mother to fetus will undoubtedly be advanced far beyond its present state.

METABOLISM OF CARBOHYDRATES

The body of the fetus is built from chemical substances which are available in the mother's blood. Energy needed by the fetus is derived from the same source. Indeed, all the prenatal requirements are met by processes of intermediary metabolism. The most readily available substance is carbohydrate in the form of dextrose which serves as the important energy source for the fetus.

Dextrose can pass from mother to fetus across the placental barrier in all mammals.[20–23] Human fetal blood-sugar concentration is always a little lower than that of the mother near term. For example, Morriss found averages of 115 mg. per cent in the fetus and 132 mg. per cent in the mother,[21] indicating that there is a gradient of flow towards the fetus. A similar condition prevails in most mammals[22, 23] but not in the pig and cow in which the concentration is lower in maternal than in fetal blood.[23, 24] The reason for these species differences is not clear, but they may be related to placental structural variations and to histotrophe as an intermediate nutriment. Much of our information has been obtained at the end of gestation or is based on averaged data of different prenatal ages. A more complete study is available in the incubating chick.[25] The blood-sugar concentration maintains a reasonably constant level up to the 16th day; thereafter it rises and surpasses the adult level at about hatching time, which is the 21st day. Fetal blood-sugar concentration varies with gestation age in mammals too. For example, it decreases toward term in the cow but increases markedly in the guinea pig and rabbit.[26, 27]

It is apparent that a simple filtration across the placental barrier is not the only mechanism governing the blood-sugar level in the fetus.

The placenta and liver are important depots for carbohydrate storage in prenatal life. As early as 1858, Claude Bernard demonstrated that the placenta contains glycogen and serves as a "transitory liver" for the embryo.[28] It has been clearly shown that the glycogen content of the placenta is high in the early part of fetal life when little or none is in the liver. Only the maternal portion of the placenta contains it.[29] A time is reached, however, when glycogen storage becomes active in the fetal liver; when this occurs there is a corresponding reduction of storage in the placenta. This crossing over takes place after the elapse of 75 per cent of the total gestation time in the rat, 82 per cent in the chick and 91 per cent in the rabbit.[29-31] The glycogen content of the fetal liver rises rapidly toward the end of gestation and is especially high a few days before birth.[22] Nevertheless, the amount of liver glycogen is inconstant at any given period in the fetus and varies with the food intake of the mother. Following 24 hours of fasting in the rat at full term, the peak of maternal liver glycogen was reached about four hours sooner than that of the fetuses.[32] When the average glycogen content in the mother's liver was 0.29 per cent of the total liver weight (fasting level) , that of the fetuses was 4.95 per cent. At the peak of storage after feeding, average values of 3.1 per cent and 10.6 per cent were found in the mothers and fetuses respectively. These differences are truly remarkable.

Glycogenic function begins after secretion of bile has started.[33] It has been thought to begin at almost precisely the time the islands of Langerhans differentiate and begin to supply insulin to the fetal blood.[26, 34-36] However, it has been demonstrated recently that the livers of incubating chicks contain glycogen at least as early as the 7th day of incubation, although the pancreatic islands do not appear until the 11th day.[36] In livers of pig and sheep fetuses, likewise, glycogen has been observed before the pancreatic islands are formed. Glycogen is distributed evenly throughout the chick liver after island tissue makes its appearance, but is confined to the cells around large veins in earlier embryos. Nearly all livers show glycogen on the seventh, eighth and ninth days and again after thirteen days, but in the intervening period fewer contain it. There is no detectable change in the blood-sugar concentration at this time of rapid glycolysis, even though the metabolic rate increases and the respiratory quotient approaches unity. These facts suggest very strongly a relative increase in utilization of carbohydrates as an energy source between the 10th and 13th days of incubation, and they indicate that the fetal liver supplies some of this material at this period during which endocrine functions of thyroid, suprarenal and pancreas are just becoming established.

The passage of carbohydrate from mother to fetus is a slow process under normal conditions, but it can be accelerated greatly by injecting insulin into the fetus.[37] When this was done it was found that the glycogen or total carbohydrate content of livers and muscles of dog fetuses was not influenced significantly. However, the lactic acid concentration of the fetal blood was raised a few hours after insulin injection and the difference between its level in the umbilical artery and vein was increased many times above the normal. About three-fourths of the dextrose which passed from the dog to its fetuses to compensate for the experimental fetal insulin hypoglycemia returned to the mother as lactic acid.[22]

The fetal dog is reported to be highly resistant to insulin and the fetal sheep and goat scarcely respond at all to doses as great as 415 units per kilogram. An insulin antagonistic substance seems to be present in their blood.[22, 23] Although insulin fails to deplete the fetal liver glycogen in dogs, sheep and goats when given to the fetuses, it has been observed to do so in rats when injected into the mother.[38] Adrenalectomy of pregnant rats similarly leads to depletion of the fetal liver glycogen.[38] Apparently the fetus practices a rigid glycogen economy at the expense of its mother's dextrose, drawing upon its own liver store only in emergencies.

METABOLISM OF LIPIDS

Well nourished fetuses are supplied with good stores of fat. Do they acquire this by transfer through the placenta or must it be synthesized from simpler materials? Perhaps the fetus is able to synthesize some from carbohydrates or amino acids, but these are not the only sources. Certain lipids are passed from the mother's blood to that of the fetus by poorly understood mechanisms and thus become available for construction of fat. To what extent lipids are oxidized by the mammalian fetus for energy is not known. They form the principal source of energy in birds during the greater part of the period of incubation.[10]

It has been quite definitely determined that the fat which is fed to a pregnant animal, and which is absorbed and stored in its tissues, does not pass through the placenta unchanged. When stained by Sudan III or some other similar dye before feeding, the body fat becomes intensely colored, but there is not the least color in the fetuses.[39-41] Regardless of the degree of saturation of the fatty acids available from material fed to the mother, the fetal fat has an almost unalterable degree of saturation.[42] It is quite different from that of the mother in respect to melting point and chemical composition, in that it contains much more palmitic and less oleic and stearic acids.[43]

Other lines of evidence suggest that there is no direct passage of lipids across the placental membranes. A marked difference in fatty acid content of maternal and fetal blood has been found. The lipid content of red blood corpuscles is about the same in infant and adult. However, the blood plasma contained on the average 948 mg. per cent in the former and 737 mg. per cent in the latter in one series of estimations.[44] Average values in another series of human newborn infants appear in Table 23.[45]

TABLE 23

LIPID COMPOSITION OF OXALATED PLASMA

	Adults mg./100 cc.	Newborn mg./100 cc.	Newborn values in per cent of adult values
Total lipids.............	589 ± 87	198 ± 80	34
Neutral fat.............	154 ± 42	90 ± 50	58
Total fatty acids........	353 ± 56	140 ± 57	40
Total cholesterol........	162 ± 32	34 ± 15	21
Ester cholesterol........	115 ± 27	20 ± 12	17
Free cholesterol.........	47 ± 7	14 ± 7	30
Phospholipid............	196 ± 23	61 ± 32	31

On the other hand, the blood passing to the fetus from the placenta is richer in certain lipids than that returning from the fetus.[46] The difference must represent lipids used or stored by

the growing fetus.   Averages of 15 analyses are given in Table
24.[46]

TABLE 24

LIPID CONTENT OF HUMAN UMBILICAL CORD BLOOD

	Artery mg./100 cc.	Vein mg./100 cc.
Phospholipid	160	204
Free cholesterol	55	64
Ester cholesterol	8	13
Neutral fat	116	121

Phospholipids are always taken up in large amounts, and
smaller amounts of free cholesterol may be absorbed by the human placenta.   Cholesterol esters pass to the fetus when they are
present in sufficient quantities in the mother's blood.   Neutral
fats have been thought to pass in both directions.   Lipids continue to be added to the static placental blood by the placenta
after birth of the child.   Without making a positive statement
concerning the mechanism involved, it may be said that a significant passage of lipids across the placental barrier takes place in
the human near term.   It has been estimated that a well nourished
fetus takes up about 50 grams of lipids a day at full term, 40 grams
of which are in the form of phospholipids.[46]

The lipid composition of the placenta and fetus of the rabbit
at various stages in gestation has been reported.[47]   The phospholipid and free cholesterol concentration increase rapidly in the
fetus up to the middle of gestation and then more slowly until
about the final week at which time the rate increases again.   Up
to the middle of gestation, the placental concentration of phospholipid decreases while that of ester cholesterol increases.   Beyond the midpoint in gestation, the reverse was found.   Slight increases in neutral fat and free cholesterol were encountered in
the placenta throughout gestation.   The results suggest that there
is a greater demand for phospholipid by the fetus than can be met
by the placenta in the middle of gestation, and a late secondary
demand which is compensated near term by increased placental
ability to supply it.

Large amounts of fatty acids are accumulated in the liver by
the guinea pig fetus.[48]   Early in gestation the liver contains about

the same proportion as that of the adult, which is approximately 2 to 4 grams; its liver fatty acid concentration is already increasing, and at a few days before birth (80 grams weight) the value reaches 15 grams per cent, while the mother's liver shows no change. It drops again to the adult level within 3 or 4 days after birth.

The lipids of the fetal liver are much more unsaturated than those in other fetal tissues and less so than those of the mother's liver.[48] One wonders whether the fetal liver is endowed with greater ability to desaturate fatty acids than is the mother's liver or if it simply receives already desaturated acids from the placenta. The latter seems the more likely, and for the following reasons.

When the pregnant animals were fasted and then given phloridzin it was found that the fetal liver storage of fatty acids was increased in the early period of gestation (fetuses weighing 30 grams and less), but no significant change occurred in the maternal liver with the dosage used. Furthermore, the fatty acid was less unsaturated than normal, as would be expected under influence of phloridzin with mobilization of the connective tissue fat to the liver. Evidently the fatty acid in the fetal liver, normally encountered, is not transported from the other fetal tissues but comes from the placenta.

Evidence has been presented recently that esterification of cholesterol by fatty acids takes place in the liver cells of the chick embryo.[49] Histochemical tests indicated the presence of free cholesterol, ester cholesterol and cholesterol-fatty acid mixtures in the liver on the eleventh day; but in chorio-allantoic grafts of the liver, in which the host was several days older than the graft, these substances appeared during the latter part of the seventh day. It is evident, therefore, that the fetal liver is prepared for its rôle in lipid metabolism some time in advance of the day it actually begins to work.

METABOLISM OF PROTEIN

A great deal of information has been obtained in recent years regarding the metabolism of proteins in bird fetuses,[10] but we still know little about this process in mammals. There are three principal methods for approaching the question. The chemical composition of maternal and fetal blood can be compared, the composition of the embryo itself at different stages of development can be determined, and finally the nitrogenous waste products of combustion in the fetus can be analyzed. We shall examine evidence obtained in these ways.

Food proteins are digested and broken down into amino acids which are absorbed into the mother's blood. These are used, not only for tissue metabolism of the mother's own body, but they serve as a readily available material out of which the fetus builds its tissues. Some of the nitrogenous food material together with nitrogenous waste products can be determined analytically as the non-protein nitrogen of the fetal blood. It has been found that non-protein nitrogen concentration of maternal and fetal blood is practically identical.[44] This suggests that the compounds in question pass through the placenta by simple diffusion.

Amino acids of use to the fetus are relatively simple nitrogenous compounds which are soluble in the blood plasma, and it is known that they are highly diffusible. The human fetal plasma at term contains about 2 mg. of amino-acid nitrogen per 100 cc. more than does that of its mother. In one 8 month premature infant the difference was greater. This makes it seem probable that simple physical processes are not the only mechanisms involved in the passage of amino acids through the placenta.

In the case of the nitrogenous waste products, ammonia, urea, uric acid and creatinine, the concentration in the two blood streams is almost identical and they probably pass from fetus to mother by purely physical processes.[44] Table 25 summarizes some of the data on human subjects.

TABLE 25

AVERAGE CONTENT OF NITROGENOUS COMPOUNDS IN THE BLOOD OF HUMAN MOTHERS AND FETUSES AT FULL TERM[44]

	Mother's blood mg./100 cc.	Fetal blood mg./100 cc.	No. of cases
Non-protein nitrogen............	25.2	24.9	35
Amino-acid nitrogen (plasma)......	5.5	7.4	10
	7.2	11.9	1 premature
Urea and ammonia...............	10.5	10.4	16
Uric acid......................	3.8	3.7	12
Creatinine (plasma).............	1.67	1.75	18
	1.70	1.73	12

Results of analysis of embryonic tissues throughout the course of gestation demonstrate that the pig builds very largely with nitrogenous compounds during its early prenatal life. The total nitrogen content of the body per unit of dry weight decreases gradually from the 6 mm. to the 50 mm. stage and then remains constant throughout the remaining portion of the gestation period. The decrease may be related to an increase of other non-nitrogenous solids such as carbohydrates, lipids and inorganic salts. At the 50 mm. stage, when total nitrogen becomes constant, the embryo may be said to have attained chemical maturity.[50]

TABLE 26

AVERAGE WEIGHT AND PERCENTAGE CONTENT OF WATER, ASH AND NITROGEN IN PIG FETUSES[50]

Embryo		Water per cent	Ash		Nitrogen		
Length mm.	Weight gms.		Wet per cent	Dry per cent	Wet per cent	Dry per cent	Ash-free per cent
2–4.......	......	97.4	.....	.....	.....	.....	.....
6–7.......	0.31	94.07	.....	.....	0.699	13.13	.....
10.......	0.50	93.37	0.558	8.43	0.861	12.99	14.18
15.......	0.93	91.38	0.775	9.00	1.061	12.31	13.52
30.......	2.21	91.14	0.708	8.00	1.103	12.45	13.53
50.......	6.55	91.65	1.036	12.41	0.910	10.91	12.45
60.......	14.85	91.05	.....	.....	0.966	10.80	.....
80.......	26.00	91.59	.....	.....	0.915	10.88	.....
100.......	72.2	91.18	.....	.....	0.95	10.78	.....
110.......	82.2	91.02	1.30	14.50	0.972	10.82	12.65
120.......	96.2	91.26	.....	.....	0.950	10.87	.....
160.......	238.57	91.71	1.349	16.28	0.891	10.75	12.84
200.......	488.0	90.34	.....	.....	1.014	10.50	.....
240.......	725.0	88.7	2.58	23.09	1.233	11.01	14.29

Interesting changes in the various fractions of the total nitrogen have been observed. No significant variation was apparent in amide, humin and cystine nitrogen but amino nitrogen concentration was increased and that of the non-amino nitrogen decreased correspondingly during the early stages. There was a fall in arginine and histidine nitrogen and a definite rise in lysine nitrogen before the 30 mm. stage. Tyrosine showed a gradual decline throughout development. Glutathione, which is thought to aid in synthesis of proteins, increased sharply until 30 mm. had been reached, after which it gradually decreased. Reciprocal ontogenetic variations in the nitrogenous substances arginine, histidine and lysine have been compared with somewhat similar phylogenetic variations.[50, 51]   They may be correlated to some extent with observations on tumor tissues, from which it appears that the younger types of neoplasms have the greater content of arginine.

Many attempts to study nitrogenous excretion in mammalian fetuses have been made without notable success. It is impossible to account for all the nitrogen excretion because the greater part is passed through the placenta, dissipated in the mother's blood and removed by her kidneys. Some, but only a small part, is excreted by the fetal mesonephros and metanephros (see Chapter VIII) and passed into the allantoic and amniotic fluids which can be recovered for analysis.

The urea content, in milligrams per 100 grams of human embryo, has been estimated to decrease as the gestation period advances.[10]   The amount of nitrogen per gram of fetus which is excreted into the fetal fluid of the ruminating mammals is likewise high in early prenatal life, but decreases sharply and then remains at a low level throughout the greater part of gestation.[52, 10]   A much clearer picture of nitrogenous metabolism of the embryo has been obtained from studies in the chick. There a closed system makes it possible to obtain all the nitrogenous wastes which accumulate in the allantoic sac.[53, 10]   Uric acid begins to collect in the allantois on the fifth day of incubation. The chick makes efficient use of the available protein, for about 96 per cent of that absorbed from the egg by the embryo during the first 13 days of incubation is retained in the embryonic tissues. Some protein is burned by the chick; in fact about 6 per cent of all organic matter used for energy during the first two weeks of incubation is protein.

One of the most interesting aspects of fetal protein metabolism is its comparative embryology.[10]   Protein materials are used for energy in much greater amounts by embryos with an aquatic habitat than by those which are terrestrial. We may classify mammalian embryos in the aquatic group with those of fishes, amphibians and many invertebrates, for they pour out their excretions through the placenta into the limitless aqueous environment of the mother's blood stream and kidneys. The terrestrial group includes birds, some reptiles (*e.g.,* lizards, snakes), arthropods (*e.g.,* insects) and mollusks (*e.g.,* land snails). Aquatic embryos excrete nitrogen principally in the form of ammonia and

urea which are very soluble and diffusible end-products and require excessive use of water for their elimination.   From a teleo-
logical viewpoint, one may say that the terrestrial forms must con-
serve water and consequently have had to devise other methods
of excreting nitrogen.   Uric acid is the end-product in these
embryos.   If birds had retained urea excretion instead of resorting
to uric acid, and if they had to store it all, their tissues would soon
become highly saturated with urea because this substance can
diffuse through the allantois into the body whereas uric acid is
retained, concentrated and precipitated within the allantoic sac
as the water is being absorbed and utilized.   In their early development birds recapitulate aquatic stages in respect to their
protein metabolism.   During the first 5 days of incubation ammonia and urea are excreted, but on the fifth day a shift is made
to uric acid and the embryo is thus spared a uremic fate.

INORGANIC METABOLISM

It is known that copper is stored in the human liver and its
concentration and absolute amount is higher there at birth than
at any subsequent time.   Its concentration is greater at birth than
at earlier prenatal periods.[54]   Copper is essential for hemoglobin
synthesis and its mobilization in the fetal liver is thought to assure
normal blood formation in the postnatal nursing period during
which the diet is deficient in this element.   In contrast to conditions in man it has been reported that the late fetal pig liver
shows no increase in percentage of copper as growth proceeds.[55]
The copper reserve of the liver is unusually low in the goat at
birth.[56]   In the incubating chick too the percentage of copper
in the liver declines from the 13th day to hatching, although
there is an increase in the actual amount present in the liver
throughout.[57]   The difference between pig, goat and chick on the
one hand and man on the other may be explained on the basis
of placental permeability.   The chick must utilize what store it
has in the egg, the pig and goat get their copper from the histotrophe, but man, having a true placenta in which contact between
maternal and fetal blood streams is intimate, may be able to draw
heavily upon maternal stores.

It has been suggested that catabolism of maternal hemoglobin
takes place in the human placenta to supply the pigment fraction

of the hemoglobin molecule intact to the fetal circulation.[58]   The iron content of the human placenta gradually increases during development.[59]   Iron is stored in the liver during fetal life and for about two months after birth during which time there is an active physiologic postnatal hemolysis.   Thereafter it declines in amount until the nursing period has passed.[54]   Iron is excreted in the bile but is absorbed again in the fetal intestines.[54]   As is true of copper, the iron reserve of the goat is low at birth,[56] and the percentage concentration of iron declines in the liver of the incubating chick.[57]   The ratio of copper to iron in the chick's tissues, other than the liver, stays constant throughout incubation.   Nonhematin iron in the tissues is small.   The metals are utilized and not stored in such large quantities in the liver for postnatal use as they are in the human fetus.

The effect on fetal rats of iron deficient diets fed to the mothers has been investigated recently.[60, 61]   The first pregnancy brought on marked depletion of maternal liver iron but there was no anemia; with the advent of a second pregnancy an anemia did appear.   The first litter of rat pups had normal hemoglobin values, but a reduction in total iron content of the entire body by about one-half the normal was evident.   The second litter exhibited a reduction of the hemoglobin of the blood and the total iron content was only one-fourth normal.   Studies in the human[62] reveal that iron deficiency of the fetus may be related to that of the mother.   Infants which are born of anemic mothers may exhibit hypochromic anemia during the first year.   The normal full term infant has a good reserve of liver iron which is probably fully as important to it as the iron it may salvage from catabolism of its excess hemoglobin during the early postnatal period.   If it were not for this fact, the human infant would probably exhibit more symptoms than it does when deprived of placental blood by the commonly practiced prompt clamping of the umbilical cord at birth.

A large series of chemical analyses of human fetuses has been summarized recently by Swanson and Iob.[62]   Content of nitrogen, calcium, iron and phosphorus throughout the greater part of prenatal life is illustrated in Fig. 69.   The retention of these materials shows a similar pattern of gradually increasing quantities.   The results indicate that there can be little demand upon the mother's

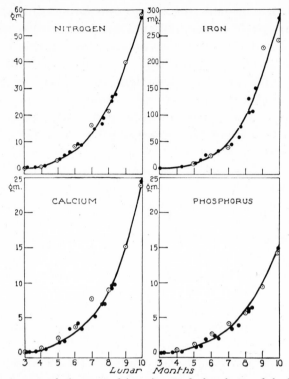

Fig. 69.—Content of nitrogen, calcium, iron and phosphorus of the human fetus between the third month and birth.   (Swanson & Iob: Am. J. Obst. & Gyn., Vol. 38, 1939, C. V. Mosby Co.)

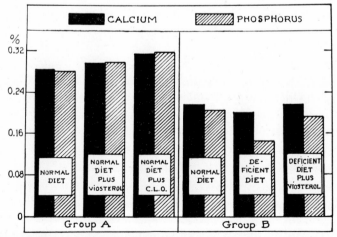

Fig. 70.—Effects of changes in the diet of pregnant rats on calcium and phosphorus content of the offspring.   (Swanson & Iob: Am. J. Obst. & Gyn., Vol. 38, 1939, C. V. Mosby Co.)

reserve of the elements in question during the first half of pregnancy. In fact it is not until the last two or three months of gestation that the fetal requirements become large.

Calcium and phosphorus are concerned in building skeletal structures. Their content in the fetus is influenced by vitamin D in the mother's diet and apparently by the amount of exposure to sunlight.[62-64] The effects of changing the diet of pregnant rats in respect to vitamin D are illustrated in Fig. 70. When the mother's diet, fortified by vitamin D, is low in the required minerals the calcium and phosphorus content of the fetal body approaches the normal level, but when the diet has in it the required amounts of the minerals plus the vitamins the fetal calcium and phosphorus content exceeds the normal. Thus the fetal metabolism of calcium and phosphorus is dependent upon that of the mother and the transmission of these substances to the fetus can be increased by vitamin D administration. In the human subject occurrence of early congenital rickets is illustrative of maternal deficiencies.[62]

Metabolism of inorganic substances other than those we have already considered has been studied less extensively. The most marked changes in all inorganic compounds are encountered in the fourth lunar month in man. Before that time the fetus contains relatively little chlorine, potassium, sodium and magnesium, but these elements show a marked increase at the fourth month.[65]

ENERGY METABOLISM

Oxygen consumption in the fetus has been studied in various species and by various methods. The most significant data relative to amount and rate of utilization have been obtained in the incubating chick and in the sheep fetus. The amounts of oxygen used and of carbon dioxide given off by the incubating chick increase in proportion to growth in size of the embryo. At six days of incubation oxygen is consumed by the embryo (exclusive of its membranes) at the rate of 0.02 cc./gm./min. This rate declines as growth proceeds and by the nineteenth day reaches 0.0134 cc./gm./min.[66] Barcroft and his colleagues[67] have estimated the rate of oxygen consumption in the sheep fetus recently by a direct method. They obtained samples of fetal blood at timed intervals after occluding the umbilical cord and determined its oxygen content. In this way they observed the loss of oxygen in respect to time and could calculate its utilization per gram of the fetal tissue without the complicating factors of the placenta and fetal membranes. Their data appear in Table 27. It will

TABLE 27

OXYGEN CONSUMPTION IN SHEEP FETUSES

Fetal age days	Fetal weight grams	Oxygen consumption	
		cc./min.	cc./gm./min.
111.....................	1,200	4.6	0.0038
126.....................	3,000	12.3	0.0041
127.....................	2,850	11.2	0.0039
129.....................	2,750	25.2	0.0081*
137.....................	3,850	20.0	0.0052
138.....................	3,650	15.5	0.0042
152.....................	2,800	16.4	0.0043*

*Authors' values; errors present but source unknown.

be seen that, although the total amount of oxygen consumed each minute rises sharply at the beginning of the last quarter of gestation, the rate of utilization remains nearly constant throughout the period studied and averages 0.0043 cc./gm./min. (excepting the 129 day fetus). This is a higher value than was obtained in earlier less satisfactory experiments in the Cambridge laboratory[68] and by other investigators who have used indirect methods of estimation. The oxygen consumption of human fetuses at terms before labor starts has been estimated to be 1.25 cc./kilo/min.[69]

The ratio of the amount of carbon dioxide given off to that of oxygen consumed $\left(\dfrac{\text{cc. carbon dioxide}}{\text{cc. oxygen}}\right)$ has been determined in embryos of several species. This, the respiratory quotient, varies significantly in the chick. Most determinations during the first five days of incubation have given values in excess of 0.7, some of them approaching unity. In vitro experiments on the five day chick have demonstrated that the quotient is 1.0 at this time.[70] Between the sixth and ninth days of incubation the respiratory quotient declines to approximately 0.7, but it rises again toward unity between the tenth and thirteenth days. These fluctuations have been taken to signify that the embryo utilizes carbohydrates almost exclusively for combustion up to five days, burns proteins very largely for the next few days and after the tenth day of incubation resorts to combustion of fat supplemented by rather large quantities of carbohydrate.[10] It should be pointed out that in the chick, which excretes uric acid instead of urea after the fifth day, a respiratory quotient of 0.7 rather than 0.8 should be expected during combustion of proteins. For more detailed information, the reader should refer to original articles.[10, 66, 71-73]

The respiratory quotient of guinea pig fetuses has been determined[74] by direct measurement of the oxygen consumption and carbon dioxide evolution of the mother and her fetuses in utero before and after occluding the umbilical cords. Quotients of 0.9 to 1.2 were obtained for the fetuses in most instances, and 0.7 to 0.9 in the mother. Confirmatory results have been obtained by others[70] in experiments using whole rat embryos in vitro (mean R. Q. = 1.04). Respiratory quotients of this nature indicate that mammalian fetuses consume carbohydrates almost exclusively in their energy metabolism.

Many investigators have studied metabolism during pregnancy, especially in man, by indirect calorimetric methods.[10] Murlin[75] observed a dog during two consecutive pregnancies, one pup being produced at the first and five pups at the second birth. An increase in caloric energy production due to the single fetus could be detected at the sixth week; it amounted to 9 per cent between the sixth and eighth weeks. The total energy produced at full term was proportional to the weight of the offspring and was about equal to that required by the newborn pups (when calculated according to the law of skin area). It amounted to 16.4 gm. cal./100 gm. in the single pregnancy and 16.8 gm. cal./100 gm. in the multiple pregnancy. The curve of total energy production of the dog and her pups showed no deflection at birth. The number of calories formed by the resting pregnant dog plus fetuses, placentas and membranes was very much the same as the sum of that produced after delivery by the lactating dog and her resting pups.

In the human not all investigators have found relationships quite so simple as those occurring in Murlin's experiments in the dog. Some[76] have reported that excessive heat production in pregnancy results from some factors other than those of fetal growth. Others[77, 78] have been able to account for all of the excess on the basis of fetal heat production, finding that the energy produced by the woman plus her fetus and its accessory structures at full term is equal to that produced by the lactating woman and the infant after birth. Recently, Enright and her associates[79] reported that a greater post-partum drop in energy metabolism than is accountable on the basis of that produced by the fetus alone occurs in 15-year-old females, amounting to about three times the probable basal energy requirements of infants. They concluded that in pregnant adolescents there appears to be some factor stimulating metabolism which results in a greater rise than occurs in more mature women. They suggested that this excessive energy production of immature girls may be related to thyroid function, and have presented some evidence that feeding iodized salt diminished the rise in metabolism during pregnancy.

One point which has not been emphasized is worth consideration. The fetus in utero is quiescent and hypotonic whereas the newborn infant is active and its muscles possess good tonus. If the energy produced by the newborn is commensurately greater than that of the full term apneic, hypotonic, quiescent fetus we will have to conclude that more energy is produced by the woman (plus the accessory fetal structures but minus the fetus) than is produced by the post-partum lactating woman. The alternative assumption is that basal requirements of the hypotonic fetus are fully as great as in the newborn infant, and this seems unreasonable.

The various calorimetric studies suggest that the fetal metabolic rate remains fairly constant throughout the latter part of gestation, but during the early period while the embryo is very small no data are available.* Postnatally the rate rises and reaches a peak at about the first or second year in the human. Similar postnatal peaks have been observed in other animals such as the rabbit, mouse and some breeds of pig; others, notably the guinea pig, show an already declining metabolic rate at birth. These facts may be related to the maturity of the heat regulating mechanisms in the different species (see Chapter VIII). They suggest

---

* Oxygen consumption of mammalian eggs during the one- to eight-cell stages amounts to 0.00073 c.mm. per egg per hour. When growth in size begins the oxygen consumption increases; on the eighth day of gestation in the rat it amounts to about 0.01 c.mm. per hour. This increases to about 0.2 c.mm. in the next two days.[80]

that the metabolic rate may in reality be increasing to some extent throughout prenatal life in man and in the other animals with a postnatal peak of heat production and may have begun to decline in the others before birth.

REFERENCES CITED

1. Meyer, R. 1925. Centralbl. Gyn., 49: 1866.
2. Grosser, O. 1927. Frühentwicklung, Eihautbildung und Placentation. Bergmann, München.
3. Grosser, O. 1933. Lancet, 224: 999.
4. Bryce, T. H. 1937. Edin. Med. J., 44: 317.
5. Wislocki, G. B. & G. L. Streeter. 1938. Contr. Emb., 27: 1.
6. Brunschwig, A. E. 1927. Anat. Rec., 34: 237.
7. Everett, J. W. 1935. J. Exp. Zoöl., 70: 243.
8. Wislocki, G. B. 1921. Anat. Rec., 21: 29.
9. Wislocki, G. B. 1921. Contr. Emb., 13: 91.
10. Needham, J. 1931. Chemical Embryology, Macmillan, N. Y.
11. Shimidzu, Y. 1922. Am. J. Physiol., 62: 202.
12. Cunningham, R. S. 1923. Proc. Soc. Exp. Biol. & Med., 20: 343.
13. Römer, P. H. 1905. Beitr. exper. Therap., 9: 18.
14. Rodolfo, A. 1934. J. Exp. Zoöl., 68: 215.
15. Mossman, H. W. 1926. Am. J. Anat., 37: 433.
16. Cunningham, R. S. 1922. Am. J. Physiol., 60: 448.
17. Bremer, J. L. 1916. Am. J. Anat., 19: 179.
18. Anselmino, K. J. 1929. Arch. Gynäk., 138: 710.
19. Schlossmann, H. 1932. Ergebn. Physiol., 34: 741.
20. Cohnstein, J. & N. Zuntz. 1884. Pflüger's Arch., 34: 173.
21. Morriss, W. H. 1917. Johns Hopkins Hosp. Bull., 28: 140.
22. Schlossmann, H. 1938. J. Physiol., 92: 219.
23. Passmore, R. & H. Schlossmann. 1938. J. Physiol., 92: 459.
24. Aron, M. 1920. Compt. Rend. Soc. Biol., 83: 631, 1445, 1447.
25. Zorn, C. M. & A. J. Dalton. 1937. Am. J. Physiol., 119: 627.
26. Aron, M. 1924. Arch. Internat. Physiol., 22: 273.
27. Snyder, F. F. & F. M. Hoskins. 1928. Anat. Rec., 38: 28.
28. Bernard, C. 1858. Ann. Sci. Nat. (Sér 4), 10: 111.
29. Chipman, W. 1902. Stud. Roy. Victorian Hosp., Montreal, vol. 1, no. 4, Gynec. 1, pp. 1–261. (Reprinted in Rep. Lab. Roy. Coll. Physicians, Edin., vol. 8, 1903.)
30. Lochhead, J. & W. Cramer. 1906. J. Physiol., 35: 11 P.
31. Corey, E. L. 1935. Am. J. Physiol., 112: 263.
32. Stuart, H. A. & G. M. Higgins. 1935. Ibid., 111: 590.
33. Sandstrom, R. H. 1934. Physiol. Zool., 7: 226.
34. Aron, M. 1922. Arch. Anat. Hist. Emb., 1: 69.
35. Potvin, R. & M. Aron. 1927. Comp. Rend. Soc. Biol., 96: 267.
36. Dalton, A. J. 1937. Anat. Rec., 68: 393.
37. Schlossmann, H. 1931. Arch. Exp. Path. Pharmak., 159: 213.
38. Corey, E. L. 1935. Am. J. Physiol., 113: 450.
39. Gage, S. H. & S. P. Gage. 1909. Anat. Rec., 3: 203.

40. Mendel, L. B. & A. L. Daniels. 1912. J. Biol. Chem., 13: 71.
41. Baumann, E. J. & O. M. Holly. 1926. Am. J. Physiol., 75: 633.
42. Wesson, L. G. 1926. Johns Hopkins Hosp. Bull., 38: 237.
43. Knopfelmacher, W. 1897. Jahrb. Kinderhlk., 45: 177.
44. Slemons, J. M. 1919. Am. J. Obst., 80: 194.
45. Boyd, E. M. 1936. Am. J. Dis. Child., 52: 1319.
46. Boyd, E. M. & K. M. Wilson. 1935. J. Clin. Invest., 14: 7.
47. Boyd, E. M. 1935. Biochem. J., 29: 985.
48. Imrie, C. G. & S. G. Graham. 1920. J. Biol. Chem., 44: 243.
49. Dalton, A. J. 1937. Anat. Rec., 67: 431.
50. Wilkerson, V. A. & R. A. Gortner. 1932. Am. J. Physiol., 102: 153.
51. Rosedale, J. L. & J. P. Morris. 1930. Biochem. J., 24: 1294.
52. Lindsay, D. E. 1912. Ibid., 6: 79.
53. Fiske, C. H. & E. A. Boyden. 1926. J. Biol. Chem., 70: 535.
54. Ramage, H., J. H. Sheldon & W. Sheldon. 1933. Proc. Roy. Soc., Lond. B., 113: 308.
55. Wilkerson, V. A. 1934. J. Biol. Chem., 104: 541.
56. Ramage, H. 1934. Biochem. J., 28: 1500.
57. McFarlane, W. D. & H. I. Milne. 1934. J. Biol. Chem., 107: 309.
58. Schick, B. 1921. Ztschr. Kinderhlk., 27: 231.
59. Hilgenberg, F. C. 1930. Ztschr. Geburtsh. Gynäk., 98: 291.
60. Parsons, L. G., E. M. Hickmans & E. Finch. 1937. Arch. Dis. Childh., 12: 369.
61. Alt, H. L. 1938. Am. J. Dis. Child., 56: 975.
62. Swanson, W. W. & V. Iob. 1939. Am. J. Obst. & Gyn., 38: 382.
63. Swanson, W. W. & V. Iob. 1935. Am. J. Dis. Child., 49: 43.
64. Sontag, L. W., P. Munson & E. Huff. 1936. Ibid., 51: 302.
65. Iob, V. & W. W. Swanson. 1934. Ibid., 47: 302.
66. Needham, J. 1932. Proc. Roy. Soc., Lond., B, 110: 46.
67. Barcroft, J., J. A. Kennedy & M. F. Mason. 1939. J. Physiol., 95: 269.
68. Barcroft, J., L. B. Flexner & T. McClurkin. 1934. Ibid., 82: 498.
69. Haselhorst, G. & K. Stromberger. 1932. Ztschr. Geburtsh. Gynäk., 102: 16.
70. Dickens, F. & F. Simer. 1930. Biochem. J., 24: 1301.
71. Bohr, C. & K. A. Hasselbalch. 1903. Skan. Arch. Physiol., 14: 398.
72. Hasselbalch, K. A. 1900. Ibid., 10: 353.
73. Murray, H. A., Jr. 1927. J. Gen. Physiol., 10: 337.
74. Bohr, C. 1900. Skand. Arch. Physiol., 10: 413.
75. Murlin, J. R. 1910. Am. J. Physiol., 26: 134.
76. Rowe, A. W. & W. C. Boyd. 1932. J. Nutrition, 5: 551.
77. Carpenter, T. M. & J. R. Murlin. 1911. Arch. Int. Med., 7: 184.
78. Sandiford, I., T. Wheeler & W. M. Boothby. 1931. Am. J. Physiol., 96: 191.
79. Enright, L., V. V. Cole & F. A. Hitchcock. 1935. Ibid., 113: 221.
80. Boell, E. J. & J. S. Nicholas. 1939. Science, 90: 411.

INDEX

ABDOMINAL muscle, 168
Absorption
  by allantois, 6, 112
  by placenta, 207–210
  by skin, 125
  by yolk-sac, 210
  in colon, 107
  in digestive tract, 99, 100, 106
    significance of, 107
  in intestine, 106
  in respiratory tract, 100
  in stomach, 106
  of amino acid, 216
  of lipid, 214
  of material swallowed, 99, 100
  of vernix caseosa, 125
Acceleration of heart, 22
Acid
  amino, 212, 216–219
  ascorbic, 199
  fatty, 213–215
  hydrochloric, 109
  lactic, 212
  uric, 112, 122, 216–219
Action potential
  cardiac, 13–16
  cerebral, 163
  from cochlea, 189
  from muscle, 176, 177
Adhesions, prevention by amniotic fluid, 121
Adrenal. See *Suprarenal gland.*
Adrenalectomy, 193, 212
Adrenalin, 194, 195
Afferent stimulation at birth, 90
After-discharge, 168
Agglutinins, placental transmission, 208
Air space of egg, gas content, 87
Albumin, serum, 118
Alkali deficit, uncompensated, 76
Alkali reserve, 66–69
Alkalinity of blood, relation to dissociation curve, 66–69

Allantoic fluid, 112, 113, 121
  volume of, 121
Allantois, 6, 112, 113, 121, 218
  relation to placenta, 6, 113, 114
  storage in, 6, 219
  uric acid concentration, 219
  vestigial, 113
Alveoli of lung, 79
Amblystoma
  behavioral development, 142–146
  comparison with man, 146
Amino acids, 212, 216, 219
  solubility of, 216
Ammonia, 216, 218
Amnion, 112, 113, 121–124, 128, 129, 147, 167, 184
  lack of nerve fibers, 128
  muscle contractions, 128, 129
  percussion of, 147, 184
Amniotic fluid
  aspiration, 79, 91–94
  composition, 112, 120–122
  excretion into, 107, 108, 112, 122, 125, 218
  experimental removal, 123
  freezing point, 120, 122
  function, 121
  hypotonic to blood, 122
  source, 99, 122–124
  specific gravity, 122
  swallowing, 99–102, 174
  utilization, 107, 109
  volume, 107, 122–124
Amyl nitrite, 20
Amylase, 109, 110
Amytal, sodium, 81
Anastomosis of chorionic vessels, 195
Androgens, 193, 195
Andromimetic function of suprarenal, 192, 193
Anemia
  cerebral, at birth, 90
  hypochromic, 220
  pernicious, of pregnancy, 52